Isabella Jackson

STORIES OF
THE DOCTOR

THE DOCTOR

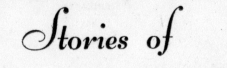

Stories of
THE DOCTOR

BY
ISABEL CAMERON

Complete Edition Containing

THE DOCTOR
MORE ABOUT THE DOCTOR
THE DOCTOR CALLS AGAIN

LONDON
THE RELIGIOUS TRACT SOCIETY
4 BOUVERIE STREET, E.C.4

DEDICATED

TO

"HIMSELL"

Complete Edition
First published April 1936
(All Rights Reserved)
MADE IN GREAT BRITAIN

AN ADVENTURE OF FAITH

HOW 'THE DOCTOR' BROKE INTO PRINT

WHEN I hear that folk are still reading "The Doctor" it makes me glad, for there was a day when I feared no one would ever read the little book—because there would be no little book to read!

I recall one gloomy November afternoon, when, with spirits to match the day, I returned from a fruitless search for a publisher in Elgin. I had already tried all possible and impossible southern firms.

The most sympathetic had said: "These sketches would only have a local appeal." The least sympathetic had reported: "We could not sell a dozen copies." (By this time 200,000 copies of the book have been sold and still the public are asking for more.)

To "himsell" I poured out my complaint. "The thing must die and the Doctor lie forgotten," I said with a sigh. "No one believes in it."

Even a douce Highland minister can have his daft moments. With the light of battle in his eye he announced: "The thing shall *not* die—and the Doctor shall *not* be forgotten. I'll lend you thirty pounds. I believe in it!"

Knowing the state of our financies at the moment I gasped but I did not protest, at least, not too loudly!

The "depression over Iceland" had departed (to Iceland we presume). This golden key would unlock the door of all difficulties. With the supreme confidence of the totally ignorant we set about publishing the book. Writing a book is a mere nothing to publishing it!

I owe an eternal debt of gratitude to the help given me by Miss Mitchell, librarian of Elgin library, a lady keenly interested in "Whatsoever things are true . . . pure and lovely and of good report." She knew what her readers read and what they should read and her sympathy, kindness and practical help were beyond all telling. Like " himsell " she, too, believed in " The Doctor ".

She knew where to buy paper, where to get a printer, she roped in a keen young artist, Mr. A. B. Beattie, and got him to make the pen-and-ink sketch which was the frontispiece of the first three editions. With brown parcel paper and red ink I designed the cover, Mr. Beattie supplied the ornamental lettering, and all this was done in a breathless hurry with our eyes fixed on the Christmas sales !

After much anxious thought and many committee meetings in Miss Mitchell's sitting-room in Elgin we decided to print five hundred copies. The booklet was to be ready in December—meantime how were we to sell it ? The printer, Mr. J. Sinclair, worked overtime and Miss Mitchell did the proof-reading ; friends on every hand.

" Try the local booksellers," Miss Mitchell advised me, and because I knew Mr. T. D. Davidson best I went first to him. He said : " I'll tell you what I'll do. If you put on my name as publisher I'll sell one hundred copies ; place the other copies ; send out copies for review ; and push the book among my customers."

For the first time I understood the importance of book reviews and of advertisements and that mysterious expression " trade terms ". Who said " Barabbas was a publisher ? " I'm here to say it's not true !

I saw the little book for the first time in a friend's house a fortnight before Christmas, and like Dickens when he saw his first article in print " my eyes were dimmed with joy and pride " and I prayed that the world would be kind to " The Doctor ".

I still possess a postcard received that week. " Sold out over the week-end ; another edition ordered "— Mr. T. D. Davidson, reporting progress from the firing line ! A third edition was called for—my capacity for astonishment was lost !

The war was now on and someone sent a copy of " The Doctor " to " That limb o' Tulloch's " who had once upon a time played " fitba' " with a syrup-tin. All that week " The Doctor " went up and down the trenches and was read with pain and pleasure by his old boys, who also demanded more copies.

A certain publisher to whom I had offered the MS. now came forward and offered to buy " the right to publish " for £25.

" Himsell ", who was always my first and best adviser, said no, and I obeyed, though I sighed too, for £25 seemed a regular fortune.

When the war was over the Doctor's friends in Canada, Australia and New Zealand began asking for copies. The manager of the Canadian Tract Society—a Scotsman—had known the Doctor and took a personal interest in pushing the sales. This might be said of all who sold it.

It was translated into German, Scandinavian, French, Braille, and Afrikaans. It is interesting to note that the German translator carefully deleted all reference to the War ! Yet two editions of the book went !

The book was now selling well, and the London publisher who had already told me that the book would have a merely local appeal sent a representative to our northern manse to capture it.

" But why ? " I asked, not unreasonably. " I offered it to you before."

" It's difficult to tell what people will like to read," he murmured apologetically.

" Not always," I replied and quoted Miss Mitchell's words and also said, not without satisfaction, " No " to his offer.

The Religious Tract Society, who had published the stories as a serial in the " Sunday at Home " came forward and undertook the publication of the book. Again I must say " Laus Deo " for publishers who are keenly and personally interested in the sale of literature that—first and foremost—will help their readers ; the money measure has been with them, as it was with all of us, of secondary importance.

"An adventure of faith" it was, and thanks to the many and kindly readers, an adventure that was successful beyond all our expectations.   May we beg an equally sympathetic reception for this complete edition of "The Doctor Stories"?

Isabel Cameron.

THE DOCTOR

BY ISABEL CAMERON

THE DOCTOR
MORE ABOUT THE DOCTOR
THE DOCTOR CALLS AGAIN
FROM A COTTAGE IN PENNYCOOK LANE
THE ADVENTURES OF ELIZABETH GRAY
HELEN ROSE AND THE CHILDREN
GILLIAN MUNRO
RED ROWANS
GORRY
BOYSIE

THE DOCTOR

BY

ISABEL CAMERON

" The pure in heart shall see God "

Twenty-fifth Edition

LONDON

THE RELIGIOUS TRACT SOCIETY

4 BOUVERIE STREET, E.C.4

Reprinted by kind permission of the Editors
of the United Free Church *Record*
and of the *Sunday at Home*

———

Photograph by Miss Grant, Elite Studio, Elgin

FOREWORD

IN sending forth this new and enlarged edition of *The Doctor*, the publisher asked me to write a Foreword. "But what shall I say?" I asked in dismay. "Oh, anything," he replied easily. "People never read Forewords, they're just put in for the look of the thing." Thus reassured, I take up my pen to thank all those who have given the little book such a warm welcome. The writing of it has been a sheer labour of love, and if I have managed to capture and to convey to the reader some stray gleams of the winsome personality of the original, then I am content.

His friendship enriched my life, and gladdened my heart, and has left an abiding memory at once gracious, tender, and gladsome. One cannot recall the Doctor without a smile creeping into one's eyes. Coming to our house as he did at a time when the shadow of illness lay on it, his is a tender and an especially warm place in our hearts. "What!" he would say in pretended amazement, when I would tell him of the invalid's improvement. "*He's not dead yet!* He's a fraud, a malingerer! I'll report him to the Presbytery!" But at evening prayers, how he would pour forth thanks to the great Father God for restoring health and courage, and how near we felt the Unseen at such moments! So, with laughter and with tears (and are they not twin sisters?) our friendship grew closer and closer.

His views of God were like himself, great and spacious. "Money," he cried one day, "it's just God's gift to His children who can't understand anything better. He

gives them money to play with, just as we give little
children ha'pennies to please them. But to His own
dear children, He gives His great gifts, wisdom and
understanding so that they see wondrous things out
of His law. These are the things that matter because
they abide." A comforting thought in these days of
materialism.

So the Doctor rests from his labours but his works
do follow him. In the Old Book he loved so well it is
written " The memory of the just is blessed."

ISABEL CAMERON,
U.F. Manse,
HOPEMAN.

THE DOCTOR'S BIRTHDAY

IT was a windy, sunny March morning. In the quiet street where the old minister, Dr. Lindsay, lived, two message boys were enjoying a game of football, an ancient syrup tin serving as a ball. The tin, with the hollow sound peculiar to empty cans, landed just at the Doctor's feet as he closed the gate behind him. He was feeling particularly gay this morning. It was his birthday, and the post had brought him all sorts of remembrances from loving friends. Perhaps the one which pleased him most was from his granddaughter, who was training as a teacher of cookery in Edinburgh. She sent him a box of cakes of her own baking, and each a perfect triumph of culinary art. "Far too pretty to eat," the old Doctor decided. "Tut, tut, why is the bairn worrying about me having to pay her fees? Silly lassie!"

His heart was warm with the thought of these things as he stepped out and found the tin at his feet. With a quick look up and down the street to satisfy himself that no one was watching him, and settling his soft hat more firmly on his white head, he gave a hop, step, and leap, and sent the tin hurtling merrily back to the astonished errand boys. These admirable youths were picking up their various baskets, with a "life-is-real-life-is-earnest" expression, but they could not repress their admiration for the Doctor's sportsman-like shot. With a yell of delight the butcher's hireling (known as "that limb o' Tulloch's") sent the tin flying back, and the Doctor, now fairly into his stride, returned it with such energy it went headlong into the grocer boy's basket, where it instantly converted a dozen fresh eggs into custard or omelette—just as you chose to look at it. The "limb o' Tulloch's" had also suffered in the fray, and the leg of mutton which had been entrusted to his tender mercies rolled helplessly in the dust. Without wasting time, he seized it and, adjourning to the nearest pump, he gave it a vigorous sousing, and then dried it with the blue-striped apron with which butcher-boys are generally girded. He thoughtfully offered the use of the garment to the grocer's loon " to wipe things wi'."

If you think the Doctor was dismayed by this accident you don't know him in the least. His was an eternal and a joyous youth, which rose triumphant over trifles. " Where were you going, my boy ? " he inquired, and his brown eyes were twinkling like a mischievous child's.

" To the Manse, sir."

The Doctor chuckled. " That's all right ! Tell the housekeeper that it was my fault, and tell her, too, that she's to give you a cake each out of the box that came this morning." By what magical sleight-of-hand both boys found themselves in possession of pennies it is not for me to say, and long before the loons had thought of suitable words of thanks he was half-way down the street.

Life became once more for these harassed and hard-working young men a grim reality ; yet were their hearts warm and grateful because of " him who passed."

The years in their flight had brought much added sweetness and wisdom to the old Doctor, but his heart was always the heart of a child. That was the reason why all children smiled when he came near them. There were two little children playing with a wheelbarrow, and as the Doctor passed he laid his hand upon the head of the smaller one. Though he spoke no word, the bairn seemed to divine that he blessed him, and so did his brother, for he came running after the old saint and said timidly, " Dae't to me, too ! "

" Dae what ? "

" What ye did to ma wee brither," the child pleaded. " Lay your hand on my heid."

Somehow the pathetic words uttered in the old time by an elder brother, as he pleaded with his father for a blessing, flashed into the Doctor's remembrance, " Bless me, even me also, O my father." His generous heart was quick to answer the appeal, and he laid his kindly hand upon the child's rough head, and blessed him.

His first call was at the house of Mary Mackenzie, a woman stricken down with a sore and grievous illness. For weeks she had been slowly dying, but to the woman, a Highlander, brought up in orthodox Ross-shire, the supremely important question was, was she one of the elect? This, more than the pain of her trouble, more than the thought of death even, oppressed her.

"How are you to-day?" the old Doctor asked as he sat down by her bedside. "No pain? And you rested well and slept for an hour or two? That is good news. The Father is dealing gently with His child."

The sick woman sighed, and the look in her eyes told more than her tongue. "It's a long, dark road I will have to be going," she whispered. For a minute the Doctor did not speak. Then taking her hand in his he said, "I mind when I was a little laddie we lived a good way out of the town, and one night I had been sent a message and it was dark before I got home. The road lay through a dark wood, and, of course, I was sure there was a bogie behind every tree waiting to gobble me up; and when I heard a footstep, then I was quite sure I was doomed; but before I could yell, I heard a voice saying, 'Is that you, Willie?' It was my father. He was looking for me when I was never thinking about him, and the road was short and as light as day because he was with me. It was only my earthly father—and he had been anxious about his boy. Don't you think, Mary, that the heavenly Father, who puts the love into our hearts, is willing to come with us on our dark roads? 'I will not leave you comfortless,' He said, 'I will come to you.' 'When thou passest through the waters I will be with thee.' "

In text after text he poured forth his soul, and the sick woman at last caught some of the ecstasy of his spirit and smiled, albeit tremulously. The tears were running down her cheeks, but it was the thaw after the long black frost.

" Mary," he said, " is it not well with you ? He's calling you ! He's saying, ' *Mary, is this you at last?* I have been looking for you for years.' "

There are those yet who remember the old Doctor's prayers—the near and dear intimate talk of a child speaking to a beloved parent—for the Fatherhood of God was ever to him the supreme thing.

Mary was sobbing softly when he finished and when Kate Murray, who lived in the other end of the house and looked after Mary, stole to the door, she was amazed to hear the old Doctor singing in his voice which was still sweet,

" When Zion's bondage God turned back,
    As men that dreamed were we."

It seemed to Kate, as she stole softly away, that she heard the clink as of coins changing hands, and she certainly heard Mary protesting, " But there is no occasion, sir. I have the old-age pension, and it's more than I ever made with spinning or knitting."

When the Doctor emerged from Mary's, he took his way round the corner and past the smithy, which was shut up. John, the smith, when he caught sight of Dr. Lindsay, instantly became so engrossed in his work (which happened to be the mending of a broken slate on the roof) that he could not even raise his eyes. His careless unconsciousness of the minister's presence was a trifle too elaborate. With quite unnecessary violence he began to hammer in a nail, and did it with such vigour that he broke the slate. It fell with a loud clatter, and John's little boy, a child of four, who had been playing about the foot of the ladder, screamed. Like a flash of lightning the Doctor darted in, and by what was nothing short of a miracle, he swept the child into a place of safety. The child's mother with a white, scared face came running out. " It's all right," the Doctor said, carrying the child into the house, " Johnnie is all right ; aren't you, boy ? "

By this time the father had descended and joined them. "Is—is—the bairn—a' richt?" he faltered.

"All right," Dr. Lindsay replied cheerfully, "neither cracked nor broken. Tell your Daddy, Johnnie, that you are all right."

John, the smith, suddenly sat down, and wiped his brow. "I . . . nearly . . . killed . . . ma . . . bairn . . ." he faltered, "I meant that slate for—for . . ."

"Ay, ay," said the Doctor comfortably, "you don't snuff, do you? Try a pinch," offering a snuff mull which on many an occasion tided over an awkward pause in a conversation.

But John, having started to confess, was determined to make a clean breast of things. "I nearly killed ma wife on Setterday," he said; "I came home drunk—you needna hide your face, Maggie, ye ken it's true, and that it was ma hand that . . ."

"Hush, hush," she cried piteously, "dinna let the bairn hear you!"

"And noo I nearly killed ma bairn," he went on stubbornly.

"I always have hopes of a man when I hear him confessing his sins," the Doctor said cheerfully. "It's the man who confesses other men's sins that I cannot thole."

He did not spare John in the talk that followed, but he sent his wife and child out of the room first. Then he dealt faithfully with the man but, like the skilful surgeon he was, he did not inflict one unnecessary incision, and very tenderly he bound up the wound afterwards.

"If you can spare the time," he was saying as he came out of the room, "you might take a look at the roof of my kitchen. There's a bit of it leaky, and you know the old word says, '*Thekk your roof in the calm.*' Johnnie, boy, could you run up to the Manse and tell my housekeeper that I sent you for some of the nice cakes I got this morning?"

And Johnnie, with a beaming face, scampered off.

Beyond the smithy, and just before the Doctor turned up the road to Sweetmeadows, he met Meg the henwife swinging along with a basket of eggs over her arm.

"Well, Margaret, how are you?" he said, stopping and holding out his hand, 'I'm glad to see that you are well, though I haven't seen you in church for some time."

Meg's manner was haughty. "I haff my reasons," she said with her nose in the air. She came from distant Stornoway, and spoke the English language in a fascinating way, agreeable to all if intelligent only to herself. "I haff my reasons," she repeated, but the frost in her manner was visibly melting, for who could withstand the Doctor when he looked at you with his friendly brown eyes?

"I am glad you have your reasons," he said solemnly (though his eyes laughed). "From what I know of you, I am sure they are good ones, too. May I hear them?"

"It is about my seat in the church," Meg burst forth. "They haff moved me from the transvaal where I wass sitting and they have put me into the seat of the merchant, and I am ferry angry, because I wass sitting yonder since the resurrection."

"And so you are not coming to church," the Doctor said musingly.

Meg grew uncomfortable. "It is not of the same quality," she went on; but what she meant, one can only dimly conjecture.

"Ay," the Doctor said in a tentative fashion, "I see." Then he cleared his throat. "Did I ever tell you why the kirk-session of Kincorn all resigned?" he asked. "Well, the reason was almost as good as yours—the session clerk's wife gave a clocking hen to the ruling elder's wife to hatch out chickens, and the hen would not sit and broke the eggs, so the wife stayed from the church and made her man stay too; and then the other wife heard of this, and she stayed from church and so did her husband, and the bairns stopped coming to the Sunday School, and the end of the matter——"

"But that was ferry wrong," Meg interrupted. "Many's the hen I haff that will not sit s'pose I wass to kill her. If that wife had had sense——"

The Doctor laughed. "Ay, if she had had sense," he echoed, "like you Margaret, and came to the church and took care of her soul and never heeded her temper."

Meg had the grace to laugh, "You must excuse me, sir, for making so free, but I'm sinking I'll be coming back to the church."

"That's right! I'll speak to the seat-letting folk to give you back your old seat."

"Not at all, not at all," cried Meg. "It wass myself that was complaining, I could not hear you sitting in yon transvaal; but I wass not wishing to sit wiss the merchant, for he once cheated me out of half a dozen eggs."

"And how much was that?" Dr. Lindsay said, putting his hand into his pocket. Meg uttered a shrill expostulation, and turned hurriedly away. "Well, call at the Manse and ask my housekeeper to give you a cup of tea, and one of my grand cakes, when you are done of selling your eggs," the Doctor called after her as they took their separate ways.

Into the farmhouse of Sweetmeadows the old Doctor came like sunshine in a November fog. The farmer had been chained to his bed with a broken leg for six weeks. In a "farm toon" the work is always "thrang" in the spring, and James Falconer chafed at being thus imprisoned, "like a tethered hen," as he expressed it.

He was full of questions as to what Burnbraes on his right hand, and Bruntland on the left, and Burnside over the way were doing; how the ploughing was getting on; how the lambs were looking, and what appearance had the young grass. And because the Doctor had spent his earliest days on a farm, he was able to answer all the questions satisfactorily.

" If I could only get my legs below me," Falconer
sighed.

" How many years had you your legs below you ? "
the minister asked with a kindly twinkle in his eye,
" and did you always thank the Lord for it ? We take
His gifts as a matter of course ; but when He withholds
one, we cry out in dismay. Oh, I know ! I do it
myself ! The other day I was out for a turn, and
because it was such a sunny morning I took my newspaper and sat down by the riverside. Well, suddenly it
began to rain, and I had neither coat nor umbrella, so
what did I do but make a hole in the middle of my
paper and stick my head through it. It came round
my shoulders like a lampshade, but it kept me dry !
Well, I was stepping home when I met a lad driving a
young horse, and at the sight of my lampshade the beast
bolted. (I think it was one of the Bruntland horses).
The lad and myself gave chase, and at last we caught
him. ' I'm afraid I frightened your horse ? ' I said.
' Frichtened the horse,' says the lad. ' You wad
frichten the very deil, going aboot like that.' ' Well,
my boy,' says I, ' I have been trying to frighten the devil
for fifty years, and he's not scared of me yet.' Neither
he is, for when I went home and felt rheumatism in my
back, the devil whispered to me that it was wonderful
how God afflicted me, and I nearly believed him till I
minded it was not God at all, but my own foolhardihood
for sitting on the damp grass."

There was a subtle undermeaning in this little story,
which James Falconer, a worthy man but perhaps a
little too worldly, was not slow to see. " When I get my
legs again," he said cheerfully, " we must see about
getting some alterations done to the church. It's a
disgrace to think how long it is since there was a lick
of paint put on it." And the Doctor, well pleased with
the result of his little sermon, took his departure.

Falconer's ploughman was standing smoking in the
barn door as he passed, and he responded gruffly to the
Doctor's genial greeting. He was one of that fast-

growing band who do not approve of ministers and scarcely ever enter a church. His manner was antagonistic and repellant as the minister paused to ask after his health.

" It's a long time since I have seen you in church," Dr. Lindsay said—" not since I christened your last baby."

The man grunted and did not trouble to remove his pipe.

" I don't approve of churches," he said sourly.

" Look at the way you ministers quarrelled over the Union. Do you mean to tell me that is right ? I'm a common working grieve, but mind, I'm telling you, I took a scunner at the kirks then, and now they're speaking aboot anither union. Well, let them go at it ! Jock Bruce and myself were near han' at blows one day here aboot this union." He paused and looked righteously indignant.

" How many bairns have you ? " the Doctor asked with seeming irrelevance.

" Six, sir."

" All christened ? "

" They are that," he replied proudly.

" You remember when you held up your children in baptism you promised to bring them up in the nurture and admonition of the Lord ; are you doing it ? "

" I'm doing it as well as most ; look at Burnbraes' ploughman——"

" We'll just look at you, William," the Doctor said quietly. " There was that nice laddie of yours who went to Vancouver (I have a letter of his in my pocket, I'll give you to read. Yes, poor boy, he sent back the passage money I lent him). Well, when he was going away, I said, ' Mind, Willie, and say the prayers you learnt at your mother's knee.' What think you did he say ? ' I never learnt any prayers at my mother's knee ; the only prayer ever I learnt was the one yourself taught me in the Sunday School.' "

William's pipe was in his pocket long ago and his face

was red as he listened. " Now, I'm an old man and
you're a young one—well, you are young beside me—
to-day is my seventy-eighth birthday—so you can take
a word of advice from me. Never mind finding fault
with the rest of the world, just try to make your own
corner of it as happy as you can. I'll be looking for
yourself and your wife and the bairns in the church
next Sunday. That's the sort of Church Union I'm
asking the Lord to let me see before I go hence. Here's
the letter, and you can give it back to me the next time
you come to see me."

The heart had died out of the day when the old man
turned his face homeward. He had grown tired and
faint, and with the shades of night a sense of his own
loneliness oppressed him. His wife had died years ago,
and his children were all in homes of their own. Before
the emptiness and desolation of his own fireside, his
bright, brave spirit quailed. " Father, take me home
soon," he whispered like a tired child, as he sat down
wearily in his chair. He shut his eyes, and for a
moment a tide of longing broke over him, leaving him
drenched and miserable.

His housekeeper tapped at the door. " Dan Angus is
in the kitchen, sir, wanting to see you ; but maybe
you'll have your supper first."

In a minute the tiredness fell from him like a mantle.
Dan had been in the " far country," and the mere fact
that he had voluntarily sought the minister, told that
Dan's face was turned once more to the Father's house.

" You did well to keep him, Janet. Bring him and
the supper too ! " he cried.

He greeted his visitor with kindness, but without any
appearance of being astonished.

The Father had answered another of his prayers, that
was all.

" Janet," he cried, " bring me the box of cakes I got
this morning."

Janet, a long-suffering and silent woman, allowed
herself one remark. " I can bring you the box——"

she said.   The old Doctor opened it and peeped among
its paper linings.   There was one small and rather
limp-looking cake left.   He took it out and handed it
to his visitor.

"You take it," he said, "I have meat to eat that ye
know not of."

THE DOCTOR "VISITS"

I

THE Doctor knocked gently at the door.

"How is your father to-day, Miss Forsyth?" he asked.

"He's real dottled kind, Doctor; come awa in an' see him."

She led the way into the sick-room. "D'ye ken wha this is, faither?" she asked the little old man in the bed. "This is Dr. Lindsay come to see you."

The old man's face beamed with pleasure. "Oh, weel div I ken him! A fine man—the finest man ye could fa' in wi'."

The daughter, with a scandalised face, turned to the Doctor apologetically. "Did I no' tell ye?" she sighed. "Ye can see for yersell how dottled he's grown! But ye needna wunner either—he's near a hunner years auld!"

The Doctor's eyes were dancing, but the rest of his face was quite solemn as he said, "I just hope when I'm as old I'll be as charitable in my judgments."

"Hoo's yersell?" the old man asked in his high piping voice. "What's doing in the toon?"

In his younger days Donald Forsyth had been a slater, and it was pathetic to hear how persistently the old man's thoughts turned back to his working days. Now the Doctor was able to tell him all about a new school which was being built near, and how the carpenters that very morning had been fixing the joists for the roof.

"The sclaters will be on gin the end o' the week," the old man said, and there was a wistful look in his face. "Man, I sometimes wad gie onything jist for the feel o' the hammer an' the nails again—an' the smell o' the new wood an' the fresh lime, an' me astride

a roof! I had a queer dream last nicht," he went on.
"I dreamt that I was young again, an' able for ma
wark, an' that I was sclating a hoose—a real bonnie
hoose, an' the maister came up to see it, an' says he,
'Are you near dune, Donald?' 'Aye,' I said. 'Aye,
sir, twa mair sclates 'll feenish'; and he says, 'That's
richt—I'm expectin' the tenant for the hoose vera
sune'—an', an'—steek the door, Doctor; I dinna want
Janet to hear—the tenant's name was written ower the
door, an' wha's think ye was it?"

He paused to search the Doctor's face for sympathy
and understanding.

"Ye're richt!" he cried triumphantly (the Doctor
had not uttered a word, but his eyes were eloquent),
"Ye're quite richt, it was jist ma verra ain!" A great
smile lit up his face as he leaned back exhausted on his
pillow.

"That was a great dream, Donald," the Doctor said
softly, and then taking his little well-worn Bible out of
his pocket, he read: "*For we know that if the earthly
house of our tabernacle be dissolved, we have a building from
God, a house not made with hands, eternal in the heavens*";
and to the old man, whose earthly tabernacle was so
soon to be dissolved, the words brought great comfort
and cheer. The Master Builder seemed very near as
the Doctor gave thanks for the home of many mansions,
and the glad, strong life of the city, where the inhabi-
tants shall not say, "I am sick," and the oldest angels
are the youngest.

The old man seemed to doze as the Doctor stole
quietly away, with a whispered word of sympathy to
the daughter so soon to be left alone.

II

The sunny street was full of children hurrying home
for dinner. How the Doctor remembered their names
was a mystery—but remember them he did—and what
was even more surprising, he remembered the sex of

the little babies, who, in charge of mother or nurse, were taking the air. No mother ever forgives you if you call her baby " it " ; it is almost as unpardonable as calling her splendid boy " she ! "

One particularly delicious little dumpling, in all the pomp and circumstance of a white starched frock, was coming towards him in charge of her nurse. She stared solemnly at her old friend, and then announced, " *Noo soos*," pointing to her toes.

The Doctor expressed liveliest admiration.

" I've a clean hankie myself," he remarked with modest pride. He drew out the large, white, silk square with which we always associated him, for he was one of the daintiest of men. Strange to say, his handkerchief came forth accompanied by a square of butterscotch ! " Where could this have come from, I wonder ? " the Doctor murmured to himself. " It's most remarkable ! I wonder are there any more squares ? "

There were ! One for nurse and one for Molly—and with many wavings of Molly's fat little hands and kisses blown adown the wind, the little company parted. A lonely old maid who lived on the other side of the street had been watching the little incident from behind her curtain. She sighed as they passed out of sight. Somehow, the street seemed forlorn and desolate now that they had gone.

III

The old pensioner who lived next door was tying up a rose tree, and the Doctor gave him a cheery greeting. " How are the roses, Peter ? "

" Fine, sir," Peter answered.

" And how's Mactavish ? " Mactavish was Peter's terrier, and loved by him as only an old bachelor can love a dog.

At this question Peter's face clouded. " That spiteful auld maid," he began.

" Meaning your next door neighbour, Miss Jane Brodie ? " the Doctor interposed blandly.

" It's her," Peter said with much emphasis and no grammar. " She threw a brush at the poor sowl o' a dowg an' got him fair in the back ! I'll have the law on her ! "

" Mactavish was meantime chasing her cat ? " the Doctor asked carelessly. Peter evidently did not hear. " It's the first time I ever heard of a woman managing to hit what she aimed at," the Doctor chuckled.

" She couldna weel miss him," the old soldier said bitterly. " She had him between her an' the water-tank."

" On the top of which her cat had taken refuge," the Doctor said shrewdly. " Aye, aye, Peter, we must live and let live. I always think of the way Miss Jane nursed her parents when they were dying. How good and dutiful she was. Her heart is gold, Peter. Yes, I believe she is a real child of God—a daughter of the King all glorious within."

" Then," said Peter, determined to have his revenge, " *them that auchts her sud flipe her !* "

It was too much for the Doctor ! His shouts of laughter brought both Miss Jane and the injured Mac-tavish out to investigate. " Dinna lat on," Peter pleaded ; but the Doctor was helplessly wiping his eyes, incapable of speech ; Mactavish, who was quite the gentleman if you kept him away from cats, joined politely in the laughter, so what else could the others do ? No quarrel can raise its ugly head amidst inno-cent gaiety. When the Doctor parted with the neigh-bours, Peter was cutting a bunch of roses for Miss Jane, while that lady was patting Mactavish on the head and calling him " Good doggie ! "

IV

The Doctor was humming a little tune to himself as he faced the country road, for he was doing his

" country rounds " this afternoon. It was a lovely sunny afternoon in June, and the world was looking very beautiful. The Doctor's face reflected the fairness of the day, and looked like a house whose open doors and windows are full of happy children and lovely flowers. Suddenly his expression changed ; it became dull and blank, as if one had put up dark shutters and closed the front door.

Coming towards him was Burgess of Burnbraes, driving into town. There are certain people who cannot be more fittingly described than by saying they are " nesty buddies," and to this unpleasant class belonged the mean-faced little man now approaching— a canine smile on his thin-lipped mouth, and the trustless expression of a ferret glinting out of his eyes.

With a great appearance of pleasure he drew rein. " I'm extra glad to see you, Doctor," he said with insincere gush. " I was determined to see you the day if I had to go to the Manse ! "

He gave a cackling unpleasant laugh, but there was no answering smile on the Doctor's face. Burnbraes shuffled uneasily in his seat, and in his heart he resented the Doctor's attitude and determined to have his revenge.

" If you have the time you might go and see poor David Anderson at the Haughs. He has been six weeks on his bed and neither minister nor elder has darkened his door."

" Aye," the Doctor's tones were non-committal, " the doctor is attending him, I suppose ? "

" Twice a day for a week or two," replied Burnbraes with much satisfaction.

" They sent a message for him ? "

" Ou, aye, the loon was once or twice for him through the night."

" Did they send a message to the minister ? "

Burnbraes had not seen what was coming and he was somewhat taken aback.

" I couldna—say—" he stammered.

" You know well enough they did not," the Doctor said sternly. " When David Anderson has a child to get baptised, he comes to church one Sunday before and whiles, one Sunday after, and that's all we see of him. When he's sick he sends for the doctor, but thinks the minister will miss him out of the church and will know by instinct that he is ill, and he will make himself believe that he's an ill-used man. Oh, I've heard David Anderson on the subject before."

" Aye," said Burnbraes, " I was sorry to hear the things he was saying about you."

" Why did you not come and tell me then ? "

" Oh, I was busy putting down the neeps, and couldna spare the time. I would excuse you, Doctor, if I was Davy, and say nothing about it ; but I was annoyed at the folks saying if it had been Gordon of the Burnside you would have been out lang syne seeing him, 'cause he's a big farmer and poor Davy is a small one, an'——"

With an uplift of the hand the Doctor silenced him. " I should certainly have missed Mr. Gordon," he said stiffly. " He's in church regularly. That I know. Whether he's a poor man or a rich one I have not the slightest idea. As a matter of fact, I am on my way to see David Anderson now. Fine weather, isn't it ? "

" Too dry—far too dry—if we dinna get rain the neeps will be spiled," replied the " nesty buddy," who was never known to be pleased with the weather.

With a coldly polite bow the Doctor went on his way, his spirit jarred and rasped by this encounter. " Such men are in every congregation," he used to say. " God allows them there for the minister's sanctification." The wind had shifted to the east, and the sun had gone behind a cloud.

V

The Doctor was walking along soberly enough now—when at the cross-roads he met a company of tinkers—brown-faced men and women and children. and, because he never could resist speaking to a baby, he must needs stop and ask the names and ages of the little folks. " This little one now ? " he asked pointing to a bundle carried by a young mother. " How old is your baby, my dear ? "

" She's only three weeks auld." Proudly she unrolled the bundle, disclosing a small red face and a pair of bright eyes. She listened with outward carelessness (but inward pride) to the Doctor's praise of her first-born, and " What is her name ? " he asked.

" She's no chrissened yet, sir," she said, and then, because for her child a mother can be greatly daring, she faltered, " Would you, sir, chrissen her ? "

The Doctor stood for a moment in thought. " Is your husband here ? " he asked.

" Yes, sir. Wull, stand forrit ! " A tall, sheepish young man came forward, touching his forelock as he came.

" And here's ma lines," said the young mother, now as brave as a lion (so to speak), and produced from some mysterious keeping place her marriage lines and the child's birth certificate.

After the Doctor had examined them he said, " Well, friends, we'll just have a word of prayer."

Overhead a choir of larks sang their rapturous song of praise. Against the soft blue of the sky the dark sombre green of the fir trees and the tender green of the birches made a fitting background for this strange little company. The brown burn, slipping softly by, seemed to croon a happy contented lilt, carrying the news to the far distant sea that once again the Master was saying, " Suffer little children to come unto Me, and forbid them not." As the Doctor stood with bare white head and reverend face, the tinker folk felt the spell of the Unseen touching their hearts. This Friend, present but unseen, to Whom the old minister spoke with such love and confidence, might they not catch a glimpse of Him too ? If they could have put their thoughts into speech they would have used the words of the old time when one said, "Did not our heart burn within us while He talked with us by the way?"

An old woman, evidently the baby's grandmother, had dipped a jug into the brown burn, and with water warmed by the sun and soft from some distant ben, Mary Stewart got her name. The baby wailed a little at the name—perhaps she knew what a tragic one it is in Scotland; perhaps it was because her father did not hold her comfortably.

The Doctor's pockets were always standing open for the benefit of those who might choose to put their hands into them, and now from one of them he took a white penny and put it into the baby's tiny hand. There was a shower of brown pennies for the other children, and then, followed by the blessings and thanks of the whole tribe, he took the road again. And because of him who passed, and tarried with them for a little while, the hearts of these poor aliens and outcasts were softened and humanised as only hearts can be touched by the winsomeness and the wonder of Divine love.

VI

At the farther end of the wood the Doctor came on Willie Gills herding a dejected-looking cow.

"How are you, Willie?" the Doctor shouted—for William was deaf beyond all telling. Often, too, he misunderstood what was said, which made conversation with him a thing of great surprises.

"Very sick, sir," he replied, evidently thinking the Doctor had asked about the cow. "So's the wife, and 'deed I'm no' awful weel masell."

"Tut, tut!" said the Doctor sympathetically.

"It's this evil new fashions, sir, that did it," Willie went on in the peculiar toneless voice of the very deaf. "If folk wad be wearing iron clamps on their heels, ma coo was well the day."

The Doctor looked bewildered. "Aye?" he shouted.

"Just that," Willie said. "Iron clamps is na good

enuff noo. Folk maun hae this *ginger rubbon* heels on their boots, an' that's what no coo can digest." He spat viciously and nodded his head. "What no coo can digest," he repeated.

"Did your cow eat a rubber heel?" the Doctor shouted. "Was that what made her sick?"

"Wha?" Willie asked. "Is't the wife you're asking aboot? She's no weel wi' eating too muckle curds."

"But what made the cow sick?"

"Sick? It's no sick so muckle as severe pain in the pit o' —— "

"Yes, yes," the Doctor said hastily. "The cow I'm asking about."

"Spent a hale day ower one boot," Willie said gloomily, " an' then near choked on the ginger rubbon heel." With a sympathetic handshake the Doctor left him, not at all clear in his mind as to which of William's household had been emulating the ostrich.

VII

There was a long dreary stretch of road to walk ere reaching the little farm of the Haughs, where David Anderson lay ill. The weary-faced woman who came in answer to his knock was David's wife, a gentle, diffident little creature whose spirit had long ago been broken by her domineering, hectoring husband.

"When had you a night in your bed?" the Doctor asked gently, clasping her hand in his own warm, friendly grip. At the kind words her eyes filled with sudden tears.

"I have aye to watch at nights," she said, with a catch in her throat; "but Davy's mendin' noo, an' sleepin' too."

"Did you ever hear, Mrs. Anderson, that ' His angels watch over him who sleeps, but with the watcher a watch He keeps '? Not lonely the night when He is keeping watch too."

"Aye, sir," she said, feeling her chafed soul already soothed, for David Anderson was an "ill" man to nurse.

The strangely sensitive spirit of the Doctor felt the hostile atmosphere when he entered the sick-room.

"So you've come at last," was the first salutation growled out by the beetle-browed man lying in bed. "Six weeks—aye, near seven—an' neither minister nor elder darkened my door."

The Doctor let him give vent to all the bitter thoughts which he had been cherishing and then when he was quite done he said pleasantly, "Well, David, you have been very frank with me, and I'll be equally frank with you. When were you in church last? Just one Sunday after I baptised your last child—and the child is three years old. Do you mean to tell me that you had duties every Sunday since then, which kept you at home? Still, when a man begins to confess the minister's faults, I have hopes of him. Perhaps—with the help of God—he may presently be confessing his own."

Very faithfully and very tenderly did he speak to the sick man, but he wounded only to bind up again. There was a shamed flush on the man's face which was all for his soul's good. His wife had crept in, and was sitting at the foot of the bed.

"When you're better, Davy," the Doctor said, "you and the good wife must go for a holiday. She's needing it as much as you. Man, do you mind to thank God for your wife? What would become of you just now without her?"

And David, who had taken all his wife's ministration as a matter of course, saw, for the first time for many a day, the tiredness of her face, and because he was not at heart a bad man, but merely a self-centred, careless one, he saw it now with pained surprise.

"You're no' tired, Mary, are you?" he asked.

"No, no, Davy," she assured him.

"Oh, these wives," the Doctor said, "they're

hopeless ! She hasn't been in bed for six weeks, but she's not tired ! " Words evidently failed him. He left behind him, as he always did, peace and harmony, and in the tender light on Mary's face he could read the dawning of a new and a happier day for the folks of the Haugh.

VIII

One more visit and he must retrace his footsteps. The Doctor was physically and mentally tired, yet at the thought of the last visit his face brightened. Angus Mackay was a Highlander and had the strange mystic seer spirit which belongs to certain Celts. For years blindness had been creeping on the old man, but as his bodily eyes failed him the eyes of his spirit grew keener and ever keener.

" You are welcome, sir," he said, going to the door ere the Doctor knocked ; " I knew your step."

He led the way into the spotless little kitchen where Merran, his wife, was busy at the baking of bannocks. " What a good smell," the Doctor said, giving an appreciative sniff. " Merran, a ' piece,' please, and a small bit of cheese."

" And what have you been doing to-day ? " the Doctor asked as he munched the crisp brown cakes and washed them down with a glass of new milk.

Angus smiled a little wistfully. " And what is there that a poor, blind, old man like me can be doing, but thinking, and thinking? "

" What were you thinking about, Angus ? Merran, may I take another cake ? "

" Well, sir, if you had the Gaelic, or I had the right English, I could be telling you."

" Go on," said the Doctor. " You needn't always be casting up my ignorance."

" God forbid," Angus said, with so much simple earnestness, the Doctor burst out laughing.

" Well, sir, I was thinking about the disciples, and how the Lord was asking them one day, ' Whom do men say that I am ? ' Fine did they know that some were saying, ' He is a Samaritan ; He is a friend of publicans and sinners ; He has a devil ; He is mad '—and the Lord knew that too. But the disciples did not tell Him that. No, no. They said, ' Some say Thou art Elias ; some Jeremias ; some a great prophet ' ; but as for themselves they knew very well that He was greater than all the prophets—He was the Christ. It was because they loved Him so much they were so wise."

The Doctor, thinking of his encounter with Burnbraes that very day, laughed a little. " Aye, Angus, if we love we will bring to the loved one only what is likely to cheer him. It must have been a great day in the Master's life when Peter said ' Thou art the Christ.' "

IX

The sun was setting behind the distant Ben Wyvis as the Doctor walked homeward through a land drenched in silence. From far away, remote, forlorn, and undomestic, came the cry of the curlews, while circling over his head in troubled flight a pair of lap-wings flew with querulous, complaining voices. Those night sounds seemed to add to the lonesomeness of the night. To the Doctor the death of a summer day was always depressing. When he reached home he sat down wearily in his study chair, and found himself longing like a sick bairn for the gladsome morning, and the stir of life awakening up to a new glad day.

Presently his housekeeper brought him the news that old Donald Forsyth had passed away, and though he expected it, yet he felt an added weight on his spirit. Long he sat brooding over the happenings of the day and the tidings which had come at the end of it. He leaned back wearily and closed his eyes. Deep sleep came to him, and then he saw to his surprise that he was standing outside a door along with a crowd of others. Soon a little group of bare-headed men carried out a coffin, and he saw the name " Donald Forsyth,"

and his age in stark, white letters on the lid. The
outward trappings of death had always pained him,
and he shuddered as he looked. Then from out of the
grim black coffin there fell a mass of corruption, un-
speakable, and loathsome ; but even as he sickened at
the sight, lo ! emerging triumphant from the rottenness,
there rose a form—young, raidant, fair, and lovely. In
ringing tones this shining one burst forth, " Ah, I knew
that I would rise again ! " In a moment earth and the
things of earth had passed, and there stood the Holy
City, with the ransomed of the Lord gathered home,
and he heard a song of matchless music, " Worthy is the
Lamb, for Thou wast slain and hast redeemed us to God
by Thy blood."

THE KING'S MESSENGER

IT was on a lovely Friday morning in June that
Dr. Lindsay set out on a pilgrimage which had for
its object the helping of a fellow-minister through his
Highland Communion. Part of the journey was by rail ;
part by the mail-coach. As the Doctor stepped out
of the train and made his way to this latter, he stopped
to sniff appreciatively the smell of peat-reek rising in
lazy, blue clouds from the chimney of a little thatched
cottage. Some starlings clustered and chattered on the
roof of the station house, and lent an every-day note to
a scene otherwise remote and solitary. From far-off
hills echoed the lonely cry of the curlew, lapwings complained (quite untruthfully) that someone was robbing
their nests, and the larks, always joyous, filled the air
with pulsing melody.

Rory, the mail-driver, hoisted the Doctor's bag into
the coach. This was followed by two sacks of mails, a
hamper of bread, sundry small parcels, and, if one might
trust one's nose, a box of kippered herrings.

"Now, sir," quoth Rory, "where would you like to
sit—in the body or on the box ? "

In the "body" was already seated one passenger.
After a quick glance at him, the Doctor chose the box,
whereupon the passenger snorted and put his legs upon
the seat. He had a squat, pump-like figure, a face
round as a moon and sphinx-like in expression, eyes
which were not neighbours, and a foolish-looking nose.
His mouth was hidden behind a forest of red whiskers.
His luggage consisted of a basket and an umbrella—the
latter a most lady-like affair with a waist. He was clad
in a suit of "blacks" made at some prehistoric date,
when he too, had had a waist.

Rory addressed him as "Maister Mactougall," and
inquired genially after his health.

"I canna complain," he replied cautiously, in a foggy tone of voice.

"Gran' day, sir," Rory began conversationally to the Doctor, climbing into his seat and gathering up the reins.

Next minute he gave an angry roar. "Weel, what now? We'll no' get started this side o' Christmas, I'm thinking!" This speech was hurled angrily at the stationmaster, who came hurrying out, carrying a huge bandbox. Rory's rage was of no moment to him. "Don't be forgetting the lassies' hats," he panted cheerily, "an' Donal the drover is asking, if you see a cattle beast on the road to let him know. Ye can tell the keeper, too, that yon ferret he sent to the Lodge is lost, an' he'd better send east another."

"Aye, aye," Rory grunted. "Ye can pit the box in beside Maister Mactougall. Any more orders?" he inquired with ominous politeness.

"No' that I can mind o'," the other replied blandly. "Good day, Rory!"

"You seem to get a lot of queer errands," chuckled the Doctor, who had been listening with keenest relish to the conversation.

Rory laughed too. "Allow me! From the penny 'purn' to a suit o' Sabbath-day 'blacks' an' a funeral hat, there's nothing but I get! *I once bought a dolman* for a wife up the Glen! I did that. You'll have heard o' dolmans, sir?"

The Doctor looked wise and nodded.

"There was another aaful thing the weemen was wearing aboot the same time—'*garrybaldies*' they was calling them. I refused to buy them for anyone, though as a rule I'm no' a blate man. I would not need to be!"

The Doctor looked wiser than ever, but no rash word escaped his lips. The subject scared him worse than it did the bold Rory.

Oh, the sweetness of the hill air as they journeyed on! Dr. Lindsay revelled in the sights and sounds and

gracious influences of the day. Rory, finding him even
thus early in his acquaintance a man after his own
heart, poured out story after story of interest. There
was the cairn where the tinker in the year eighteen
hundred and ever-so-few perished in a snowstorm ;
farther on was a big iron-clamped stone where a witch
had been burned ; yonder was the ruin of a castle
called, to begin with, Blackhall, but after a wild fight
with a cateran clan, changed to Castle Rhuig (Red),
and you can guess what the *red* was. Then there was
the ford of the Kelpies, weirdest of all places, for there
one might see that—

> " Knee deep she waded in the burn,
>   The Banshee robed in green,
> She sang yon song the whole night long,
>   And washed the linen clean.
> The linen that would wrap the dead,
>   She beetled on a stone,
> She stood with dripping hands blood-red,
>   Low singing all alone,
> ' The linen robes are pure and white
>   For Fergus Mhor must die to-night.' "

" Man, that's fine," the Doctor said warmly, when
Rory had finished, and not without dramatic power
(for Rory was a Celt !) what is surely one of the eeriest
of Gaelic poems.

A hollow groan from the " body " made the others
aware that their fellow-traveller did not share these
sentiments.

" Are ye no' feeling aaful weel ? " Rory inquired
kindly. " Maybe sitting with all that o' weemen's hats
is no' agreeing with you ? "

There was no reply to this sally, and, looking at
Rory's face the Doctor was surprised to see the twinkle
die out of his eyes and an angry frown pucker his
forehead. He muttered something angrily below his
breath and made a (comparatively speaking, for his was

the kindest of hearts) wild lunge at the off-horse's flank.

"Haud up, there, lad!" he bawled angrily to the astonished horse. "It's a fine day, Kirsty," this last to a woman who was walking a little ahead of the coach.

The woman turned and looked meekly at the driver, as she wiped, not without ostentation, the moisture from her brow. "It is a fine day, as you say, Rory, but aaful warrum. You'll no' be feeling it up there, but if you wass walking! The sun fair takes the heart out o' my legs. Yet see you how disappointed I would be if I did not get west to the church!"

Rory sighed resignedly. "You'll better be coming up here then, and be keeping company to Maister Mactougall."

Very promptly did Kirsty avail herself of this none-too-gracious invitation. "May the Lord reward you, for I cannot," she said. Having thus got rid of all financial responsibility, she settled herself to have a talk with her fellow-traveller. Rory snorted and made a certain dark allusion to folks who were so mean that they would skin the very—but I had better not finish the sentence; Rory was a homely soul!

From Mr. Macdougall, now, Kirsty received a welcome that was almost enthusiastic. His one eye beamed —if there was a certain sternness in the other, it was certainly not for Kirsty.

"Wass you going to the sacrament?" he inquired in his peculiar foghorn tone of voice.

"I wass indeed," Kirsty replied. "I wass there on the Fast day too."

"And what sort of diet did you get? Wass it edifying?"

"Is that what you're saying?" Kirsty cried shrilly.

"You would be understanding him?"

Again Kirsty could only shrilly echo the question, adding piously, "The Lord forbid that I would be understanding the decent gentleman!"

Rory looked at the Doctor's face, then both men

looked hastily away at some distant object, and Rory remarked, apropos of nothing in particular, "Allow the weemen, just you allow them ! They're the boys ! "

"And where wass you, Maister Macdougall, since a long time ? There's a very long time since I didn't see you."

"I was away at Portree."

"At Portree ! Think of that now ! At a sacrament ! "

Mr. Macdougall nodded. "What other, Kirsty ? "

"And who wass you staying wiss—if it's not bad mainners to be asking ? "

"I wass staying wiss Mistress Macleod."

"Doesn't myself know her very well ! "

"A fine woman," cried Macdougall, "a fine, fine woman ! "

"She would be showing kindness to the stranger ? " Kirsty hazarded shrewdly. This worthy "stranger" waggled his head—words were utterly useless, at least English words, for the rest of the conversation was carried on in an undertone and in the Gaelic language.

"What sort of a day did you haff on the Friday ? " Kirsty inquired in her best "company" voice, perhaps feeling uneasy over what a Highlander always regards as a lapse of good manners.

"Grand ! " replied Macdougall. "There's yonder o' men the minister can lift, as many as five-and-twenty ! "

Kirsty rocked herself ; whether in admiration or envy one cannot tell.

Not unnaturally the Doctor was puzzled to hear of a minister whose merits seemed to outshine those of a circus acrobat. Rory, however, explained, in a whisper, that what he meant was that on the "Men's Day" or Friday, some question in theology is discussed by the men ; in this particular case there were twenty-five men willing (if not able) to take part in the discussion.

They were now fast approaching a brae, and Rory,

with almost unnecessary briskness, ordered his passengers in the " body " to alight.

"Keep your seat, sir," he said to the Doctor, in whom long ago he had recognised a kin spirit. Dr. Lindsay, however, would not hear of this favour, and descended with the others. He and Rory ʻtrudged on, slightly ahead, the Doctor humming softly, " Hold the fort," and seeming to derive much satisfaction from the verse which begins with " See the mighty host advancing ! "

Whether this apparently innocent melody had anything to do with Mr. Macdougall's decision to take a short cut over the hill, it is not for the historian to say. The fact remains that both he and Kirsty somewhat hastily took their departure—and " Thanking you kindly for your lift," this last from Kirsty.

"That'll no' do much to feed my horses," Rory remarked as they passed out of earshot. " Aye, sir, they're going to Clachan. Gorry Glen is a good bittie farther west. Ye can get up tae your seat again."

The next stopping place was Gorrybeg, and here Rory handed out his first mail-bag to the little, timid-looking woman waiting for it.

"Hoo's the coo ? " he inquired genially. " Yes, oh yes, I have the salts for her. Don't be giving her a too big dose an' keep her off the new grass for a while. A parcel ? What kind of a parcel, Mistress Macpherson ? "

"It was a bittie o' beef I was getting from Mackay the butcher in the town," she explained artlessly.

"Mackay the butcher, said ye ? " cried Rory, diving into all sorts of keeping places. " Would you, sir, be so good as to haud the reins till I have a look for this parcel ? Wait a wee now ; here's something, from Mackay, too ! Is that it ? No, no, that's a pair of cork soles from Mackay the shoemaker, for that wife at the toll house, her wi' the ʻ romantic fivir ʼ—that's no' it. Cork soles would no' be as good as a beefsteak, though indeed the last beef I got mysell was as teuch (tough) as any cork soles. Would it be a big parcel ? "

"Jist a pound of boiling beef, Rory," the gentle little voice said, and suddenly it struck the Doctor that Rory was not in any particular hurry to find the parcel.

"Try your pockets," he suggested, with a twinkle in his eye.

Rory did.

"Weel, weel!" he exclaimed, "am I no the amadan (fool)? In ma pooch all the time! Here you are, Mistress Macpherson. No, no, it's no bother in the world. How I forgot to look in ma pooch is more than I can think!" Thus with amazing artfulness did the gallant Rory put by the time with little Mistress Mary Macpherson, Postmistress of Gorrybeg!

There was a certain constraint in his manner as they took the road again, but though perhaps the Doctor had glimpsed Rory's love-tale, there was nothing but warmest interest in his manner as he listened to the story.

"There was a time, sir, when she hadna a puckle meal in the house. I'm that glad she can buy beef now an' then."

"Aye," said the Doctor sympathetically. His manner invited confidences.

Rory nodded.

"Her man died, a poor feckless body at the best; he went and died at the beginning o' harvest, leaving her with nothing between her an' the poors' hoose, but the coo, an' even she was dry! An' little Sandy, her boyan, was just getting better o' whooping cough."

He paused as if considering the perversity of a man who would choose to die at such an inopportune time. "The coo was dry, as I said, an' hardly a blade o' grass left; you'll mind o' the summer o' drought we had five-six years ago? Weel, it came to be that poor Mary had neither bite nor sup in her hoose one morning, and the craiter was like to give up in despair. 'You'll be going to the hill with the coo,' says she to the child, 'An' will I be getting my breakfast when I came back?' says he, an' poor Mary had to let on she was not hearing him. Weel, Sandy went off with the coo, an' Mary she's to her knees. Have you the Gaelic, sir ? No ? Weel, weel, it's all the same. When she came to the place where you say, ' *Tabhair an dhuinn n-aran laitheil*,' in the English that means, ' Give us this day our daily bread,' wasn't there a chap (knock) at the door. And who was this but big Donald, the keeper from the top of the Glen ! An' says he, ' How are you the day, Mistress Macpherson, an' will you be so good as to give me a drink of water ? An' if you would please to throw this packet of sangwidges to your hens, an' empty the tea out of this flask, I would be aaful obleeged. You see, I'm going up the hill with the shooting gents, an' they always take so much meat with them, I'm wearied carrying it.' Aye, an' when the little fellow came home from the hill it was the fine breakfast his mother had waiting on him ! "

The Doctor's eyes were bright with sympathy. " He is faithful that promised," he said softly.

" Aye, an' more than that," Rory went on. " Donald the keeper spoke to His Grace aboot Mary, an' he gave her the Post Office an' a free hoose an' grazing for her coo, an' now she's able to buy her beef an' all her orders an' to send Sandy in his new kilt to the school with the other bairns."

The Doctor seemed to be turning something over in his mind. " You're a married man ? " he inquired.

Rory's face was always red, but it seemed to become a trifle redder as he stammered, " N-n-no, sir."

" Too young ? " the Doctor inquired wickedly.

Rory gave a great roar of laughter. " No, sir ; but—but—jist aaful blate ! "

And what followed after that is a secret, which only the Doctor, Rory, and one other person know.

. . . .

The welcome Dr. Lindsay got was rapturous when he reached his journey's end. The minister's wife had belonged to his congregation in her girlhood's days ;

indeed it was partly for her sake he had undertaken this long journey.

"Why, Katherine, is this you?" he cried as she came hurrying down the garden path to meet him.

"And who else could it be?" she asked gaily.

"*I thought it was a lady*," he replied solemnly (but his eyes twinkled!).

"That's because I put on my best frock in your honour," she assured him, and then they both began to laugh. The sight of his face, the sound of his voice, and the old delightsome banter unlocked such floods of fond, glad recollections that if she had not laughed, then she would certainly have cried.

"Are you very tired?" she inquired presently. "You must go straight to bed, whenever you have had dinner."

"I won't," he replied firmly. "I won't be put to bed like a bad baby because, forsooth, you have a house of your own. Impudence! Where's that boy of yours?"

Before she could answer, a little boy of about four years came marching to meet them. He advanced bravely, a sturdy, untidy little figure in a ragged kilt, and clutching in a grubby small fist a certain culinary utensil known to Kate-of-the-kitchen as the "tattie chapper." Within a few feet of the Doctor he stood stock still, earnestly scrutinising the old minister's face, then, flinging aside what was presumably his club, this primitive man advanced with beaming face and outstretched hand.

"Peta 'ikes 'oo," he announced.

"And I like Peter," replied the Doctor promptly, for it is thus, with simple directness, deep calleth unto deep!

"Katherine, please, my bag. Do you like elephants, Peter?"

"The kind God makes?" the child asked. "Meat ones?"

The Doctor's face fell.

" Come, now, Peter, be reasonable. You wouldn't expect a little baggie like this to hold a real meat elephant. Watch what happens when his head comes off."

Behold, when the obliging beast was decapitated, his interior was stuffed full of sweeties ! A very prince of elephants !

" And where's Himsell ? " the Doctor asked when he could spare a minute from Peter. " And is dinner nearly ready ? I'm famished. If you don't give me something to eat I shall have to begin with ' *boy* ' and end with ' *elephant*,' eh, Peter ? "

But just as Mrs. Mackenzie was explaining that this was the " Men's Day," and that they would not wait for Himsell, the door opened to admit the minister.

" Surely you could not have had five-and-twenty men to lift like the stalwart of Portree ! " the Doctor laughed, and then he related what he had heard in the mail-coach. The meal was a merry one, and the younger minister, who had been feeling his spirit somewhat chafed with all the worries of a Highland Communion, presently found himself wondering why, in all the world, he had been fretting over what were trifles. He " smiled to think God's greatness flowed around our incompleteness ; round our restlessness His rest." That was because the Doctor sat at his table, and from before his presence all nagging, rasping irritations vanished.

In spite of lusty protestations, he was bundled off to the study couch to rest till tea-time, and Peter, with Jumbo in his arms, went about on tip-toe, making the most elaborate attempts at walking quietly that were ever beheld.

.   .   .   .

On Saturday, Dr. Lindsay, just to assert his independence, insisted upon accompanying Mr. Mackenzie to the Gaelic service in the evening. It was followed by a distribution of " tokens," and a meeting of the kirk session.

"Will David Macintyre be coming forward?" the Doctor heard one elder ask, and because the question was in English he found himself listening for the reply. In some occult fashion, he sensed a tragedy behind the words, and though the reply came in Gaelic, he knew it was unfavourable. William Sutherland, the elder, a man who had continually lamented the present-day depravity, though he did nothing to improve it, sighed dismally and shook his head.

"Backslider!" he groaned.

The Doctor's generous heart was immediately on the side of the absent backslider. His rich and varied experience in church work had taught him the importance of prayer and patience, but before he could utter a word Mr. Mackenzie came up to him. In a low voice he said, "I fear this meeting is likely to last for some time. We have a case of church discipline before us. Would you mind going into Donald the catechist's house and waiting for me? He is a saint; you'll enjoy a talk with him. I'll call for you whenever we are through. Just open the door and go straight in. He is ill, unfortunately, otherwise he would be here to-night. You remember how we came from the Manse? Well, instead of going all that way, turn to the right at the cross-roads; you can't miss it."

The Doctor took his hat and his departure, just pausing at the door to say, as if thinking aloud, "Charity suffereth long, and is kind." William Sutherland, righteous-over-much, scowled evilly to himself.

The evening air felt like a benediction after the heated atmosphere of the meeting-place. The setting sun was filling the strath with glory. The Doctor paused at the cross-roads to ask himself, "Did he say the left hand or the right?" Because the left-hand one went the way of the setting sun, he chose it. Presently he found himself in front of what was unmistakably a carpenter's shop and house. Remembering the instructions, he lifted the "sneck" of the house door and entered.

"Who's there?" cried a gruff voice.

"A messenger of the King," promptly replied the Doctor, making his way into the kitchen. The owner of the gruff voice was sitting by the fire and eyed him in no friendly fashion. His wife, busy at her baking board, became so flurried she began to knead her bannocks "widdershins" instead of "deasoil"—that is, against the sun instead of with it—a forbidden ritual in the baking of bread! Yet there was nothing in the presence of the kindly stranger to cause any uneasiness.

"Mr. Mackenzie told me to wait here till he would join me," he explained, looking for some place to put his hat. The woman came forward timidly, placed a chair for him, and took possession of hat and stick.

"And how are you?" the Doctor asked genially of the dark-browed man. "I am glad to see you are able to be out of bed. Your minister told me you were bedridden."

"I might be in my bed or in my grave for all that him or any of his elders care," the man said sullenly. The Doctor was puzzled by his reception, but if you think he was daunted, then you don't know Dr. Lindsay in the least. Quite clearly he had come to the wrong house, yet it was not the wrong house either, for here was a man imprisoned in a bond of bitterness, and the Father had sent him to set the prisoner free. With a quick prayer for guidance, the King's messenger sat down and spread out his hands to the blaze.

"Do you know, I'm quite glad to see a fire, though it is the month of June," he began conversationally. "I haven't seen a peat fire like this since I was a bairn going for holidays to my granny's in Strath Dorran. I can remember yet the taste of the bannocks toasted in front of——"

"Strath Dorran!" the man interrupted with great excitement, and in a flash the Doctor knew that his prayer for guidance had been answered, and that the Father had put into his hand the key of this man's prison house. With another swift prayer for further guidance, he turned to meet the man's questioning eyes. Like grey ghosts at cock-crow, all the bitter thoughts with which the house had been peopled fled and the atmosphere became at once peaceable and friendly.

"Div ye ken Strath Dorran?" the man asked, and his speech was the speech of a Lowlander.

"My granny lived there. I used to go there every summer for holidays."

"Ye—ye'll no' be ony freen tae auld Mrs. Begg of Inverdorran?" the man whispered fearfully.

"I'm her grandson," the Doctor nodded, smiling.

"It cowes a'," the man said, still speaking in the same fearful voice. "Div' ye mind on David Macintyre the vricht (wright)?"

"Don't I?" the Doctor chuckled. "He gave me my first boat—a beauty it was too!—called 'The Running Rill.'"

The man gave a little sigh, whether of pleasure or of pain who shall say, for are they not twin-brothers?

"He was my father," he said slowly and simply. Words, after all, are unhelpful things at moments of great crisis. The two men shook hands, their faces shining.

Then followed a flood of reminiscence and question. It was "Do you mind the Dorran Burn? And where's your brother Jamie? Wasn't he the loon for the trout? And where's Helen, your sister? I mind how she could climb trees. And what's your name? I think I remember you, though you cannot mind me—you were a baby in frockies then!"

When had the kitchen rung with such happy laughter before? Even Jean, the shy wife (because she had not the good English) found herself joining in it, as she softly laid a meal on the table.

"But what's your name?" the Doctor repeated.

"I'm David, sir; called after ma faither."

David Macintyre; where had the Doctor heard the name before? Like a flash there broke in on his

remembrance the scene in the meeting-house, and the
cruel, relentless face of old William Sutherland. Clearly
the Father had guided him here. " I will bring the
blind by a way that they know not," he thought.

" Tell me, then, Davy, how it came to pass that you
are living here ? " For a moment the man's face
clouded, as he explained how, by a series of strange
happenings, he had married a glen-woman, and had
settled down in her father's business as a carpenter.
He had been a lonely man, for even the speech of the
glen folks had been to him a hidden thing, and as for
the workings of their minds, that he had never even
faintly comprehended. Yet all this could have been
borne if the little son who had came to them when
they were both somewhat late in life had been spared.
" He was only seven, when "—he paused and choked—
" When he went home," the Doctor said.

There was a tense silence for a few minutes, and then,
like a burn in spate, out came the flood of bitterness
which had been gathering in the heart of David Macintyre for six long, weary years.

His sorrow for his child—his one and only son—was
great, and what sorrow is there like it in all the world ?
The old minister had died ; Mr. Mackenzie had not
come, and William Sutherland, the elder, had taken it
upon himself to visit the bereaved couple. With many
groans and moans William had asked them what
evidence had they that their child was one of the elect ?
They would like to think, no doubt, that he was, but
how could they tell ? At first the stricken father did
not comprehend what William was driving at, then the
elder quoted, " ' Whom He did foreknow He also did
predestinate ; whom He did predestinate He also
called.' Read your Bible, David Macintyre, and don't
take it upon yourself to say you'll see your child again."

" The wife there fented," David said drily, " and I
put the elder oot o' the door, an' I said—" he paused, his
throat working convulsively.

" Aye, aye," said the Doctor musing aloud and

affecting not to see David's emotion. " And one shall
say unto Him, ' What are those wounds in Thine hands ?
Then He shall answer, ' *Those with which I was wounded
in the house of My friends.*' You surely didn't believe
that the Heavenly Father would do what no earthly
father would do ? "

" It's this doctrine of election," David groaned. " If
wee Davy is no' one of the elect, then I'm no' seekin'
to gang to heaven. I wadna be nane contentit."

" Oh, hush, hush, man ! " his wife said in a fright.

" An' I'll no hush then ! " he stormed. " For sax
years I've been like a man in prison, ma heid tellin' me
ae thing an' ma hert the tither. Oh, sir, tell me the
richts o't ! " It was a sore cry wrung from the throbbing
centre of the man's heart.

" Poor soul ! " the Doctor said pitifully. " Oh, Davy,
do you not understand that election is the rock on which
we stand—not, thank God ! the door by which we
enter. You understand that, don't you ? Why, in the
days of His flesh, there were some who would keep back
the bairns from the Lord. They didn't call it the doctrine of election, they said it was troubling the Master.
What He said then is what He says now and always,
' Suffer the children to come unto Me, and forbid them
not.' "

The man's face was knit with agony, yet as he listened
to the gracious words of the King's messenger a softer
expression crept into his haggard eyes.

The Doctor's memory was always a source of pride to
us, and now, very softly and very perfectly, he repeated :—

THE MAISTER AN' THE BAIRNS [1]

The Maister sat in a wee cot hoose,
   Tae the Jordan's waters near ;
An' the fisher fowk crushed an' croodit roon',
   The Maister's words tae hear.

[1] This little poem was written by William Thomson, born in
Glasgow, 1860, died 1883.

An' even the bairns frae the near-haun' streets
 War mixin' wi' the thrang,
Laddies an' lassies wi' wee bare feet
 Jinkin' the crood amang.

An' ane o' the Twal' at the Maister's side
 Rase up an' cried alood—
" Come, come, bairns, this is nae place for you,
 Rin awa hame oot o' the crood."

But the Maister said, as they turned awa',
 " Let the wee bairns come tae Me ! "
An' He gaithered them roon' Him whar He sat,
 An' liftit ane up on His knee—

Ay, He gaithered them roon' Him whar He sat,
 An' straikit their curly hair ;
An' He said tae the won'erin' fisher fowk
 That croodit aroon' Him there :—

" Sen'na the weans awa frae Me,
 But raither this lesson learn,
That nane'll win in at Heaven's yett,
 That isna as pure as a bairn ! "

An' He that wisna' oor kith an' kin,
 But a Prince of the Far-awa',
Gaithered the wee anes in His airms,
 An' blessed them ane an' a'.

. . . .

O Thou Who watchest the ways o' men,
 Keep our feet in the heavenly airt,
An' bring us at last tae Thy hame abune
 As pure as the bairns in he'rt.

Of what followed we may not here speak, but when
at last the Doctor rose to go, he left behind him the
peace of God.
 " I'll be looking for you to-morrow, both of you, at

the Table," he said. " Well, David, you may come and give me a Scotch convoy."

Meantime in the Manse there was a great anxiety as to what had become of the Doctor. When Mr. Mackenzie had called at the catechist's house, it was to be told that the Doctor had not called there at all. Concluding that he had gone straight home, the minister followed, only to be told that the Doctor had not returned.

The session meeting had been a long and trying one for Mr. Mackenzie. Some of the elders, more eager for the letter of the law than for the salvation of souls, had urged that the communion roll be purged of the names of David Macintyre and his wife Jean, who had absented themselves from the means of grace for six years, without giving any reason. After a veritable Waterloo, it had been arranged that the minister, for whom little things of this sort are invariably reserved, should call upon the erring ones and reason with them. Frankly speaking, the prospect did not attract the minister, to whom David Macintyre had ever shown his most distant and repellant manner. He had had visions of asking his wise old friend to accompany him on this difficult mission. Judge, then, of his surprise when, in going forth to look for the Doctor, he beheld him coming strolling along the road in deep and intimate conversation with the very man whose case was causing him so much anxiety. At the foot of the garden they parted, after a warm handshake, and took their separate ways. The Doctor was humming softly to himself, " He comes the prisoners to release."

. . . .

A Highland Communion Sabbath is much more of a great " occasion " than a Lowland one. For one thing the services are double, so while Dr. Lindsay officiated in the church in English, Mr. Mackenzie took the Gaelic service in the meeting-house.

The day held a holy hush—it seemed as if even

Nature knew it was God's own day. From far and near the folks gathered. It is rather a pretty custom which requires that every woman shall have on her best and newest garments to do honour to the day, and that every man who possesses a black suit and a tall hat shall don the same on the Communion Sabbath. White shirts, too, are the order of the day, at once the pride and despair of their wearers (who have been known to go home with their stiff collars in their pockets, to the scandal of their women-folk and their own vast comfort).

The little band of elders, all clad in their decent best blacks, sat beneath the pulpit, the solemn and sacred elements spread on a linen-covered table before them. A strange custom prevails of leaving the tables empty until the time comes to "serve" them. Then, with slow and reverent tread, the members come forward to "remember their Lord."

The Doctor preached, as only he could do, on the words, "*What think ye, that He will not come to the feast?*" Very clearly he proved that He had come to this feast, that His presence filled the house on this His holy day. After a rapturous hour, he invited all those who loved their Lord to take their places at His table.

Whilst the members were coming forward, Angus the precentor chanted line after line of the 116th Psalm. "I love the Lord, because my voice," Angus sang in strange tuneful voice. "I love the Lord because my voice," the congregation echoed. So on line after line the sweet song was sung. The tables by this time were almost full. The Doctor had come down from the pulpit, and was standing among the elders.

"Yet there is room," he said, as the last note of the psalm died away. "We shall sing other four lines beginning at the words, 'I'll of salvation take the cup.'" Again the strange chant rang through the church. Angus had reached the words, "On God's name will I call," when a couple sitting near the door rose, and with downcast faces and beating hearts took the places they had left empty for six long years.

" I'll pay my vows now to the Lord," chanted Angus, and two new voices, rather tremulously, sang the words after him.

Something had moved the Doctor. He stood, a notable figure with his splendid reverence and dignity, and with a strangely uplifted expression on his face. A solemn hush filled the church. Women trembled, they knew not why, and men gripped their jaws lest they shame themselves. Then the Doctor's voice began to read, " For I have received of the Lord that which also I delivered unto you, how that the Lord Jesus the same night in which He was betrayed took bread," and so on through what is surely one of the most solemn and soul-searching chapters in the Bible. " With desire I have desired to eat this passover with you before I go hence," were the words of his " Table address."

In the prayer which followed the Unseen seemed very real, very near. Old Granny Bruce, the deafest woman in the parish, said afterwards, " I did not hear a word he said, but I knew the Lord did, *for He was nearer him than I was*, and I was in the front seat."

The sacred elements were now uncovered, and with reverent hand the Doctor handed them to the waiting elders. " This is My body broken for you. This cup is the new testament in My blood—this do, in remembrance of Me."

Slowly and carefully, down either aisle, the elders filed, bearing in their hands the vessels of the Lord. After all had been served, the Doctor, still standing among the elders, said a few words to help and sustain the members when the world and Monday morning should claim them again.

Like a great shout of triumph, and to the stirring notes of " Effingham," the last psalm was sung. " Oh thou, my soul, bless God the Lord." David Macintyre, moved and inspired, lifted his eyes from his book to meet the understanding eyes of the Doctor, fixed upon him. Then he sang in his rich bass voice, and everyone knows the rapture of the bass of Effingham :—

> " Who doth redeem thy life, that thou
> To death may'st not go down."

. . . .

At night the church was crowded, a sight to gladden and inspire any preacher, and when that preacher was Dr. Lindsay, then you might prepare for a feast or a " diet," to use the old expressive Scottish word. His text was, " He hath sent me . . . to preach deliverance to the captives," and the love and fatherhood of God were his theme. Rory the mail-driver had walked six miles to hear the minister to whom his heart had gone out on Friday, but whose name, strange to say, he had not heard. Enthralled he listened, elbows on the book-board and eyes fixed unwinkingly on the preacher's face, afraid almost to breathe, lest he might lose a single word.

The service past, like a man in a dream he went forth to lie in wait for his crony, Dugald Macgregor, who had been wont to boast most outrageously about a certain minister he had once heard.

" Man, yon's preaching for you ! " Rory exulted. " I knew he could do it ! Ach man, if that minister you're always blowing about could preach like him we heard the night, then you might well mention it."

Dugald listened with the utmost patience, and then, with a sly twinkle in his eye, he said coolly, " Yon *iss* the minister I'm always blowing about, and can ye blame me ? Yon, then, Rory, is Dr. Lindsay for you ! "

In the house of David Macintyre the Doctor was saying a few words of farewell. He was accompanied by—William Sutherland ! It was not to the house of David Macintyre alone that the King's messenger had brought liberty on this memorable Sabbath day.

" Last night, David," the Doctor said, and his face

was rapt, "I had an audience of the King, whose messenger I am. I told Him about you, David, and I prayed that He might come to the feast to-day. As I spoke with Him I noticed that standing close beside Him, clinging to His hand, was a little boy—yes, just such a little boy as that." He nodded towards a little faded portrait hanging over the mantelpiece.

Jean Macintyre, her face working piteously, uttered a little sob. "Oh, Davy, Davy voch (little) !" she whispered passionately.

"Ay, it was just Davy," the Doctor went on. "'This little boy is rather lonely,' the Lord said to me, 'for six years he had been coming with Me to My feast at Gorry Glen, hoping to see his father and mother there.'"

David Macintyre, with set jaw, got up suddenly from his seat by the fire, and faced the window. There is something awesome in the grief of a strong man, and for a few tense seconds no one spoke, it seemed as if no one dared to breathe.

Presently the Doctor's voice went on softly ; "'You'll meet them to-morrow,' I said. The bairn was glad, and the Lord said, 'It's what Davy and Myself have been waiting for.'" The Doctor's voice sank to a whisper. "And I saw them both at His Table to-day."

David Macintyre suddenly turned round from the window, and his face was the face of a man who has glimpsed some heavenly vision of which it is not lawful to speak.

"I—I thought I saw Davy, too," he whispered slowly. "It was that time when you said, 'Yet there is room,' and Jean and masell came forward."

The Doctor nodded. "He was there, with the Lord, just as he'll be there, with the Lord, when we gather into the feast above. Here, we see but as in a glass—darkly ; but—there,—face—to—face !"

DAVY'S DOG

LITTLE DAVY, the minister's five-year-old boy, lay ill. Folks said (though not to his mother) that the child was dying. For ten long days now he had lain in the grip of some mysterious childish ailment. A racing pulse, a soaring temperature told of the enemy which was eating away the boy's slender reserves of strength. Sometimes he would rave and toss about wildly, spending with the prodigality of delirium the strength he needed to fight his illness. Then again, spent and wan-faced, he would lie back on his pillow with closed eyes. At such times it seemed to his anguished mother that Davy's soul was adventuring forth into uncharted seas, whither his mother could not follow—whence he himself might never return.

" Speak to me, Davy," she pleaded in a whisper.

But the child never stirred ; his blue-veined eyelids might have veiled dead eyes, so little sign of life was there.

He remained like that all the evening. The doctor thought that possibly to-night the crisis of the illness might come. " If we can keep down his temperature and get him to sleep, Mrs. Sutherland, I think we 'll pull him through," he had said.

He had left mother and son about eight o'clock. Now it was growing late, and still Davy seemed to be in a semi-conscious state.

Then, about midnight, he began to toss and to mutter to himself. When he opened his eyes there was no gleam of recognition in them, and all at once a wave of desolation and loneliness broke over his mother's heart. Up till now she had been, outwardly at least, brave. But to-night—to-night there was no courage left in the heart of her. It had been raining all the evening, with the steady persistence which one sometimes sees in a June evening. Perhaps that was depressing her.

Then her husband was away doing chaplain duty in a southern port. Kind neighbours had offered to come and sit with the sick child, but she would not hear of this, and now suddenly she wished there was someone with her to share this anxious vigil.

Dr. Lindsay had come to take her husband's place. What he was to her during those dark days, only those who knew the Doctor in their day of trouble can realise. Still, he was an old man, and she hesitated about disturbing him.

There was something awesome in being the only person awake in a sleeping house, and unconsciously, as time went slowly past, her movements became more noiseless, her voice more of a whisper.

"Drink this, Davy, my lammie!" She held a spoon to his lips.

With an impatient fling of his arm the child sent spoon and glass flying with a crash against the table.

"Davy wants his Davy's dog," he said suddenly. "Please, please."

"Yes, darling," she whispered bravely. "Take this to please mammy first. Davy mustn't make a noise. You'll waken Dr. Lindsay."

"Davy wants his Davy's dog," the little voice insisted. And then he began to cry and wring his hands. It was agony to see him wasting his strength, but the mother was faced with a problem which was insoluble. Just then Dr. Lindsay stole softly into the room.

"No, the noise did not waken me," he assured her; "I was not sleeping. I want to know how you are now, David," he said, laying upon the child's hot, restless, little hands his own cool one.

The child stopped his distressing crying and whispered: "Please, I want my Davy's dog—now—this instant moment." The little voice was shrill by the end of the request.

His mother went to the window and stood looking into the dark night. She could see in her mind's eye the little green mound beneath the apple tree, where

Davy's dog had been buried. The very day the child had fallen ill, the dog he loved so well had been killed by a passing motor lorry. He had been Davy's insepar- able companion, when—the one a baby, and the other a puppy—they had rolled about and played unending games in the garden. It seemed to her in her present mood an ominous and a dreadful thing that Davy's dog should have left his little master. There was no dog like Davy's dog, a lovely sable collie with a white ruff about his neck, and a tail as feathery as an ostrich plume. And now the child was calling for the dog. If he were not satisfied, she knew the consequences would be fatal. " The child must be kept quiet," she had been told. It was a cruel thing that in the hour of crisis Davy should have set his heart upon what was so hopelessly impossible.

" What shall we do ? " she asked, desperately turning to the old Doctor.

" Davy wants his Davy's dog," the persistent little voice wailed.

The mother took a photograph of a happy-faced, bare-legged laddie with his arm round the neck of a collie, and tried to put it into the child's hand.

" Here is the pretty picture of Davy and his dog," she said with attempted gaiety. " See, darling, the photograph we got taken for daddy."

The child thrust it away angrily.

" Davy wants his real dog," he said firmly.

As she replaced the picture on the mantel-shelf it seemed to mock her. That handsome dog—gone ! And the bonnie bairn—was he to go also ? Suddenly she hid the photograph behind the clock. It was unbearable.

Meanwhile the old Doctor was kneeling beside the bed, his face buried in his hands. The room became full of the voiceless currents of prayer—agonising prayer, for well did the old man know how critical was the situation.

When he looked up his face was calm and tranquil. " My dear," he said in his fatherly way, " do you think you could get me a cup of tea ? Yes, yes, of course, Kate gave me supper ; but that was long ago. Ages ago ! " He nodded towards the clock. " It'll soon be breakfast time ; it's half-past two. No, madam ! I won't go back to bed ! I want tea and toast." There was a twinkle in his eye as he added, " an egg too ! I'll call you if I think Davy needs you. *Don't come though, till I call.*"

Full well did the wise old man know that in occupation Mrs. Sutherland would find a little respite from her anxiety. Well did he know, too, that her Highland nature, with the instincts of hospitality inculcated in it from her earliest fore-folk, would express no astonishment at his request.

" I think I could eat two rounds of toast," he remarked blandly, and opened the door for her.

Outside the closed door she stood. Every nerve in her body was strained to listen. The little wailing voice rang out in a peculiarly forlorn fashion. " Davy wants his Davy's dog," again and again.

" God help us," she agonised. " Oh, God, help my bairn."

The rain was falling with steady monotony on the roof. It was the hour when Nature herself is at her feeblest. Night was busy with the article of death, and day had not been born. The mother shivered as she moved about the ghostly kitchen, where the old, everyday things seemed unfamiliar, unreal. She thought of one of Hans Andersen's fairy tales, where he tells how the kitchen utensils, when human beings are fast asleep, frolic and play and boast of their high birth to each other. She must remember to tell Davy about this when he was better ; he loved fairy tales. Listen, was that Davy calling ? Like a grey ghost she glided up the stairs. Davy was still wailing.

The Doctor had asked her to do a hard thing, she told herself. Why should he have sent her out of the room when Davy might be needing her ? Ah, but Davy did not need her ; that was the cruel part of it. It was for his dog he wailed. That was cruel. God was cruel. He had forgotten to be gracious. Her heart was bitter. Floods of black despair swept over her soul. Outside in " the dead unhappy night, the rain was on the roof."

Kate, the maid, had " rested " the peat fire, and with the tongs, always the most important fire-iron on a Highland hearth, Davy's mother set the peats on end and fanned them into a cheerful blaze. As she filled the kettle at the sink in the window, she heard a strange noise, almost like a distant rocket—not so loud as the big guns, yet having in it something sinister and uncanny. Just at the moment, too, the hall clock gave the peculiar " birr " with which it always gave warning of its intentions, and the strokes one—two—three ! rang out. Her first thought, of course, was of Davy. Had he heard the strange distant boom ? Had it frightened him ? She would just run up once more and see. But Davy's soul was wandering in places where no earthly sound could reach him. He was calling, calling, calling, the same pitiful wail.

Coming downstairs again, the mother saw through the uncurtained hall window, the one which looked towards the sea, that the searchlights were out. Their great golden swords crossed and uncrossed, piercing the gloom, sending now a shaft of light over the land, now flinging one into the lap of the sky. There was a great naval base on the other side of the firth, and the folks had grown used to hearing guns booming out at all sorts of hours ; to seeing searchlights flashing ; to seeing the restless battleships passing to and fro. Yet this night seemed, to the anxious watcher, to be full of strange influences. The powers of darkness were abroad, and were warring with the powers of light. She shivered as she crouched on the hearthstone, waiting for the kettle to boil.

II

It was the wheezy clock which wakened her. How awful ! She had been asleep for a whole hour ! Had

the Doctor called? Was—was—how was Davy? For
a minute or two she felt bewildered ; her mind refused
to act. Davy—yes, it was not a dream ; Davy was ill
upstairs and she had slept. Upstairs she flew, and
stood listening once more. Silence deep, intense,
restful, was there. Softly, as softly as the dawn was
now stealing over the land, there was borne in on her
the conviction that all was well with the child. She
almost fancied she could hear his quiet breathing. It
was hard to stay outside the door, yet the Doctor had
made her promise not to come till he would call. How
had the Shunammite woman passed the hours while
another Man of God had taken her little son into his
keeping? Had she spent the night listening at the
door?

The rain had ceased. The world was bathed in
tremulous, golden light. She opened the front door
and let the blessed light in. The black night had
flown—thank God. Nothing is so unbearable in the
daytime as it is at night. From the drenched garden
stole the fragrance of sweet briar and honeysuckle.
Overhead a lark was singing with matchless melody ;
from some distant farm town a cock greeted the sun with
cheery briskness ; up from the sea came the tang of salt
seaweed. And even as she stood by the door drinking
in the sweet moist smells there pattered up the path a
collie-dog—a sable collie with a white ruff round its
neck, an ostrich feather for his tail !

In the half-open door he paused and looked in with
the " please-may-I-come-in " expression which belongs
to all polite collies. He was not Davy's dog certainly,
but no two dogs could possibly be more alike.

" Come, doggie," she said, and held out her hand.

The animal, with his eyes full of friendliness, advanced
with a smile and a wave of his tail.

Then, just then—for God never comes a minute too
soon—she heard the noise she had been waiting for all
night long, the sound of the opening door and of the
Doctor's voice.

" Come, doggie, come along," she whispered, and both ran upstairs. " Is—is——" she panted, her eyes devouring the little face on the pillow.

" Did you bring Davy's dog?" the child asked anxiously.

For answer she made him put his little wasted hand on the dog's head.

With a rapturous little sigh of supreme satisfaction he whispered, " *Davy's dog!*" That was all—but it was enough. There was a look of deepest content on the little face as he turned on his side and fell asleep, to sleep through the long hours which were to bridge the gulf between death and life.

And the old Doctor? His face was the face of a man who had been on the mountain tops with God. Serene and happy were his eyes, but no ways surprised. The loving kindness of his Father was no new thing to him.

" It is the Lord's doing and it is marvellous in our eyes," he said softly.

Then with gracious words did he pour out his heart in prayer. Thus in the old time did the Man of God call an anxious mother and say, " *Thy son* "—" *and she fell at his feet and bowed herself to the ground.*"

As he was leaving the room, his task done, she looked up with a very April face to say :

" Your tea, Doctor? It's all ready."

" Tea ! " he echoed with a twinkle in his eye. " I had forgotten. You take it, my dear. My meat is to do the will of Him that sent me."

And the explanation? Marvellous, yet simple with the simplicity of all great things. The noise Davy's mother heard at three o'clock, which had sounded like a rocket, was the noise of an explosion on board the battleship, *Beltane Queen.* The public learned in due course that the captain stuck to his ship to the very last, and his constant companion, a sable collie, stayed, too. When a boat hurried to the rescue, the captain lifted his dog and threw him into it. " Get a good home for him *someone,*" he begged. But the faithful dog, madly struggling, plunged into the sea again and tried to rejoin his master. What became of him? Was he sucked under with the sinking vessel? Dr. Lindsay and Davy's mother have their own thoughts as they look at Davy, a tall, lanky, big-eyed Davy playing with a sable collie. "*The Lord's doing—and marvellous in our eyes.*"

THE DOCTOR "SUPPLIES"

THE lights burned low in the smoky station lamps. The Saturday crowd who awaited the arrival of the last train, shivered and shuddered in the keen east wind which blew in snell and pitiless from the sea, scarce a hundred yards beyond the station. The night was dark; and in the sky not a friendly star was to be seen.

"It'll be snow gin mornin'," an old fisherman prophesied; "that bank o' clouds to the nor'ard is snow, and that's the airt o' the win' the nicht!" As the folks peered through the darkness they saw at last the bright lights of the incoming train, and heard the engine lift up its voice in welcome if unmusical greeting. "At last," Mrs. Urquhart said to herself, with a sigh of relief.

The crowd of passengers descended from the train, and for a minute or two she found herself unable to get out of the spot. She looked anxiously along the row of open doors, but she did not see the stranger she had come to meet. Quickly she examined carriage after carriage, but in vain. No one the least resembling a minister was to be seen. Along in the outer darkness of the guard's van she heard a fisherwoman pouring out effusive thanks to some unseen person. "Thank you kindly, sir, I can manage fine now. It's no' too heavy—I've many's a time carried far mair," she was saying. Then as she passed out of the station, creel on back, Mrs. Urquhart noticed a tall figure looming behind, tying the flaps of his tweed cap underneath his chin. With a feeling of thankfulness, which only the dwellers in a Manse who are faced on a Saturday night with the problem of "no supply" can understand, she went to meet the welcome stranger.

"Dr. Lindsay?" she asked timidly.

"'Dr. Livingstone, I presume,'" answered the tall stranger, and the aptness of the repartee unlocked a flood of laughter. In the flickering lights she could see his eyes twinkling merrily. "And who are you?" he inquired. "You are not Stanley, are you?"

"No," she admitted; "I'm only the minister's wife, and I've come to meet you. Here's a boy who will carry your bag."

No one who has ever shaken hands with the old Doctor can forget the warmth and friendliness of that clasp. "You had no business to come out on such a night," he said severely. "Well, boy, you may carry my bag, but I can't allow anyone but myself to carry this." "This" was a white paper bag, which, judging by the careful way he carried it, must contain something precious. "How are your bairns?" he inquired suddenly.

"They are very well," she answered. "How clever of you to know I had bairns."

"You would wonder at the things I know," he replied with a waggish look. "Although we have never met before, I know lots of things about you. I know, for instance, that your husband is ill, and that's why I am 'supplying' for him. How is he?—or don't you say in the Highlands, 'How's himsell?'"

"Himsell's getting better," she answered gaily—the night had grown, she thought, much milder; "he's hoping to be home next month. How did you know I'm Highland?" she asked; "I thought I had no accent."

"I never met anyone yet who didn't pride themselves on having no accent," he chuckled. "'Thy speech bewrayeth thee!' Did you ever hear of the Captain of the steamer in which a famous Scotsman once crossed to New York? They were great friends, and as they were nearing Sandy Hook the Captain said, 'Weel, sir, I hope I'll hev the pleasure o' your company on the return voyage. Ye ken I come frae Scotland masel'; it wiss on the tip o' my tongue to tell ye, but I jest thocht I wad never lat on and then tak' ye by surprise!'"

The old Doctor's way of telling a story cannot be

reproduced in cold print. One had to hear him and to
see him, too, to appreciate properly his art.

As they walked along he asked tenderly and sympathetically for the sick husband, and by the time the
Manse was reached they felt as if they were old friends,
for had not their acquaintance begun in the freemasonry
of laughter, the surest and quickest of all paths to
friendship.

"Where are the bairns?" he demanded the minute
they got indoors. As the little folks came, in response
to their mother's call, they, with the quick intuition of
childhood, hailed and welcomed a new friend. He
knew their names in a trice, ay, their pet names too;
he knew their ages, and the things they liked and the
things they did not like. Even Bobby, the Manse dog, an
animal of supernatural sagacity and a variety of breeds,
greeted him "like a long lost brother" as the Doctor said.

"Come away," he cried gaily, leading the way into
the dining-room, "come and see what's in this baggie!"
They gathered round him with happy, excited faces,
and of the little group the Doctor was certainly the
blithest and the youngest. Not since the grim shadow
of the minister's illness had fallen on the Manse had
there been such gaiety. And the contents of that
precious bag? Chocolate animals, butterscotch, a toy
bull dog of ferocious aspect (it was only Bobby's sense of
politeness which prevented his biting this fearsome
beast), sweets of large and satisfying dimensions!
What bliss!

The meal which followed partook more of the nature
of a feast than of an ordinary diet, and that not because
the fare was anything great or grand, but because the
Doctor sat at the end of the table and kept everyone
happy and laughing. How he discovered Bobby's
weakness for sugar no one could tell, but the knowing
little dog was discovered beneath the Doctor's chair
crunching a lump of sugar with noisy enthusiasm, and
laughing at the jokes too.

In the midst of the fun the postman's ring sounded

through the house, and the maid handed in a long flat parcel. Mrs. Urquhart took a hasty glance at it and saw that the writing was her husband's ; then, determined to " mind her manners," she laid it on the sideboard. The Doctor's bright eyes had quite taken in the little scene, and after a minute or two he said with a pawky smile, " Is that a parcel from himsell ? "

Mrs. Urquhart blushed guiltily. Perhaps " minding her manners " had not included keeping her eyes from wandering wistfully to the parcel ! " Would you like me to cut the string ? " he inquired, opening his penknife. " As a rule I'm against sinful waste, but under present circumstances (you've gazed longingly at that parcel ten times !) I think we're quite justified in being reckless." The wisdom of the man ! In a twinkling the string was cut, the paper off, and a blue card-board box came to view. Now, if you expect to hear that the minister's wife got a diamond pendant or a string of pearls, you had better read no more of this homely tale ; for what was lying there wrapped up in tissue paper was nothing more nor less than a white silk blouse and a pretty scarf !

And because that stupid woman had been feeling wretchedly anxious and worried about " himsell," and a little forlorn too, she felt her eyes fill with sudden blinding tears as she peered into the box. The Doctor did not see this, of course ! " Tut, tut, tut," he grumbled. " The idea ! the extravagant man ! " He was fingering the wonderful garment as gently as if it were a new-born baby. " The silly boy," he went on ; " why, he might have bought vegetarian cookery books for the cannibals, or picture hats for the Esquimaux— or—or—let me see now—why, bombs for the suffragettes, with his money—but what does he do ? Buys a blouse for his wife instead ! I'll report him to the Presbytery ! You won't, of course, be wearing it to-morrow ? " he asked anxiously.

" But indeed I shall ! " she flashed defiantly.

He sighed and shook his head. " I'll pray for you,"

he promised. " I'll pray that this hand-maiden *be not puffèd up !* Well, well, is that a letter I see below the wonderful blouse ? Just let me hear how he is—and then would you like me to have worship before the little folks go to bed ? "

God seemed wonderfully near that evening as they gathered round the table, Bibles in hand. The Doctor got the children, one by one, to read a verse, and then he asked the maid—he knew her name already—to read one too. When the youngest boy read in his clear high voice that " the ' Scribes and Paraphrases ' came to Jesus," it did not seem such a deadly mistake—because the smile on the Doctor's face was wholly tender. In the prayer which followed, he wrapped the little band in loving petitions—that their eyes might be kept from tears (one at least of his hearers knew why he thus prayed). " For earthly love which binds husband and wife, parent and child, brother and sister, we thank Thee," and then ended with his favourite petition, " Take us under the shadow of Thy wings, that there we may abide all the days of our life until the end." The hush and spell of the Unseen filled the room and made it a holy place as he poured out his heart to his Heavenly Father, just as fully and as freely as a child speaks to a loving earthly father.

．　．　．　．　．　．　．　．　．

Sabbath morning dawned clear and cloudless. The snow had evidently changed its mind and had gone elsewhere. The sea sparkled merrily in the sunshine, and a courageous lark was singing joyously in a field near the Manse. " This is the day which the Lord hath made," the old Doctor read, and then lifting his eyes from the Bible he gazed out at the sunny world. " And it's like Him," he said reverently, and as if thinking aloud, " It's like Him ! "

Of the old Doctor in the pulpit I feel I cannot speak. He came before the congregation with the careful fruit of his week's study—the old truth new minted, and

bearing upon it the stamp and sparkle of heaven. His
text was, " Sir, we would see Jesus," and before his words
the folks swayed like corn in an autumn breeze. A
little boy, sitting in the Manse seat, suddenly slipped
his hand into his mother's and whispered, " Is he seeing
Jesus ? Surely he's seeing Jesus. I wish I could see
Him too ! " Yes, if the pure in heart see God, the old
Doctor was certainly seeing Jesus, and many a soul that
Sabbath morning felt the sin and sorrow, the tiredness
and the weariness of the past, smitten away, as they too
drew near to catch, if they might, a glimpse of Jesus.
Recapturing the joy of their first coming, they said once
more, " Sir, we would see Jesus." It was a great day.

In the evening the church was packed. The crowd
inspired the Doctor, and never, even in his younger days,
had he preached with more passion and fervour. " And
He showed me a pure river of life clear as crystal," and
" Let him that is athirst come . . . and drink." He
bracketed the gracious words, and from them wove
such a wonderful appeal that hard indeed must the
heart have been which did not respond. As the folks
sang the closing psalm they showed they had been
moved and touched. They sang with their hearts, and
that is the best of all singing ;

> " A river is, whose streams do glad
>   The City of our God ;
> The holy place, wherein the Lord
>   Most High hath His abode."

The old Doctor stood in the pulpit singing too, the
light from the pulpit lamps shining down on his reverend
white head and saintly face, and, as he lifted his hands
in blessing, it seemed to the breathless crowd that his
face was as the face of an angel.

> " Oh, may we stand before the Lamb
>   When earth and seas are fled,
> And hear the Judge pronounce our name
>   With blessings on our head,"

T.D.   N

he pleaded, and a great inarticulate " Amen " welled
up in every listening heart.

As the Doctor walked to the Manse after the service
he suddenly became conscious of overpowering weariness. " There is no preaching without the shedding of
blood," he thought as he slowly went home. A young
man who had been in church that evening was coming
behind him, and because his heart had been thrilled and
touched by the service, and because the Doctor always
brought out the best in everyone—that young man, who
was naturally a shy and diffident youth, said, as he
came alongside the minister, " Sir, will you allow me
to offer you my arm ? I am going your way."

The Doctor's tired face blossomed into instant and
joyous youth.

" My dear boy, how good of you ! Certainly I'll be
glad of your arm. Do you know," he lowered his voice
and spoke confidentially, " I'm like the devil, I'm old ;
but I'm not infirm, only a little tired." Certainly no
one hearing his merry laugh would think he was either
old or infirm.

" I'm like the devil in another way," he went on,
evidently finding much pleasure in these comparisons.
" I must be in earnest for my time is brief. Ah, my
boy, what an opportunity I had to-night to speak to all
that crowd of young folks, and how I prayed the Father
that He would give me the right word to say to you all ! "

They walked on in silence, and just because the young
man's heart was so full, his obstinate tongue refused to
help him with so much as a single word. Perhaps the
Doctor understood, for presently he began speaking
about the wonders of the stars. A new moon, a lovely
crescent, hung in the sky, and a golden star swung over
its cup. Astronomy had always fascinated him, and
he delighted the listening lad with his marvellous knowledge of this science, for the old Doctor was always a
scholar.

" Well, my boy, here we are at the Manse gate, and
I've enjoyed the walk. You must tell me your name,

and I'll send you a little book on astronomy, seeing you are interested in it too. Write me any time you think I can help you in any way. It will give me great pleasure." And it was no idle promise, as the future proved.

The Manse children had begged as a special favour to be allowed to sit up and have supper with Dr. Lindsay, and now as his step sounded on the garden path they flew to open the door, headed by Bobby. One helped him off with his coat, another relieved him of his umbrella, his gloves were pulled off—I grieve to say that afterwards Bobby was seen to suffocate himself with one, under the impression it was a rabbit ! The Doctor's slippers were toasting inside the fender, and his energetic little friends unlaced his boots and thrust his feet into the warm slippers before he had had time to fetch his breath. When he did he quoted with twinkling eyes :

> " And now if e'er by chance I put
>   My finger into glue,
>   Or madly crush my right-hand foot
>   Into my left-hand shoe
> I weep . . ."

But he got no further, for with a shout of delight the children saw that they had indeed crushed his " right-hand foot into his left-hand shoe," and they proceeded to put matters right.

Supper past, they gathered round the table, and I wish I could show you the Doctor and those happy young folks around him, and how each in turn read a verse ; and then how the Doctor asked, could someone play a hymn, and how someone could, and did, and how the voices old and young joined in the sweetest of all the psalms :

> " The Lord's my shepherd, I'll not want."

Then with a short word of prayer, commending all

E 2

loved ones to the Shepherd who " neither slumbers nor sleeps," the Doctor finished.

.   .   .   .

After the children had gone to bed, he and Mrs. Urquhart sat by the study fire and talked. It is only those who have had the privilege of spending a Sabbath evening with him who know what a delightful thing that was. He was a man of widest sympathy and most generous disposition. He was far too big souled to descend to petty jealousy, and his warm appreciation of his fellow-ministers, and loyalty to his Church, were among his most lovable traits. His spirit loved to dwell on heaven and on the life there. Dr. Barnardo's life had just been published, and speaking of it he said : " I have no time to read it, much as I should like to ; but no matter—when I get to heaven I'll hear all about it from Dr. Barnardo himself."

" May I put my feet up on the side of the mantel-piece ? I can tell from those marks that ' himsell ' is allowed to do so. Thank you. It gives the dog more room, you see, and it rests my back, and also gives me a chance to show off my grand new socks." And then he told her the story of the socks.

Some time before he had been visiting in the country. The night was dark and the way long, and he suddenly bethought him that by crossing a burn he might shorten his road. Alas, the burn was in spate, and the plank which usually served as a bridge had been washed to the further side. This did not " daunten " the Doctor in the least, and with an " Ouch " at the coldness of the water he waded to the other side. His way now took him past the farm of Burnside, but ere coming to the farm-house he had to pass the ploughmen's bothies. He heard, as he approached the nearest one, the notes of " a cheery wee melodeon " played with much taste and a fine disregard for time. In a lull in the music he tapped at the door, and was bidden " Come in." When he opened the door he saw gathered round a cosy wood fire three or four young fellows listening to the musician

who sat in state on the table. The lads looked a little
" blate " when they saw a minister, but before his genial
smile the awkwardness soon fled.

" Will you let an old man dry his feet at your fire,
boys ? " he asked.

Would they ? The boys rose as one man, and in a
trice the Doctor was seated in front of the roasting fire ;
the musician leapt off his perch and began rummaging
in the " shottle " of his kist for something which he
presently offered—not without blushing ; the herd loon,
who had been whittling a whistle out of a " sappy sucker
frae the muckle rodden tree," knelt down and undid the
wet boots and set them on the hobs to dry. The
cattleman, who was a married man and initiated in
domestic mysteries, took the wet socks and wrung them
out at the door. It was then the musician screwed up
courage to offer his treasure. It was a pair of socks of
chaste and quiet colours (green and red), and round
their tops had been woven by some magic art the
touching words " Remember me." The Doctor donned
them with great alacrity, for there was no one who could
more graciously accept a kindness—a much more
difficult business than bestowing one !

Then they talked, and you can guess who was the
merriest there. The musician, with outward humility
and inward pride, played the Doctor's favourite tune,
which was—but no ! that was to be a secret ! Then
the talk came round to work days and rest days, and
the day of rest, and how did they spend it. The little
company were serious now, for the native dignity of the
Doctor always kept everyone in his own place. " I'll
read a chapter with you, boys," he said, " and then I
must be going." Again it was the musician who dived
into his kist and brought out a Bible wrapped in a piece
of tissue paper. The Doctor examined it carefully. " I
would like to see it looking as if it were oftener used, my
boy. I see it was your mother who gave it to you. Did
she tell you to keep it wrapped up in your trunk ? Is
she still alive ? "

"No, sir. Yes, sir." Robbie Kemp, horseman and musician in ordinary to the farm of Burnside, answered.

In the prayer which followed, the Doctor prayed that he and they, their fathers and their mothers, might meet in the Homeland to which we are daily drawing nearer, and the listening lads resolved that come what might they would go to church next Sunday and write home to the old folks too.

By this time the boots and socks were dry, and while the Doctor was getting into them, Willie, the herd loon, vanished suddenly. He came back in a minute with his stable lantern in his hand, and was nearly felled by the musician for his pains. "I'm to take my bicycle lamp," he whispered fiercely. "Be off and supper your bastes."

I do not know how many of the lads convoyed him home, nor how many lamps they carried—the Doctor would never tell. "But there!" he added triumphantly, "these are the socks that Robbie Kemp's sweetheart made for me, and I'm prouder of them than a gardener's dog with a rose in its tail! I'm to marry them, too, whenever Robbie can get a married man's place, and I think I know a farmer that's needing just such a man as Robbie."

That was the story of the socks, and it was not difficult to read between the lines, nor to guess that because of "him who passed by" that evening and turned aside for a little into the bothy of Burnside, the whole course of Robbie Kemp's after-life was altered.

"But I must be going to bed," he said, glancing at the clock. "Can you give me the change for half a crown before I go?"

"No," she said promptly, "I can't"; and then, greatly daring, she said, "You know you don't need change for half a crown. You have your return ticket."

The Doctor threw his eyes and hands ceiling-wards. "Did ever any mortal hear such impudence?" he inquired of some unseen hearer. "I don't need change, quo' she! Well, well."

" No, you don't," she repeated. " You are just wanting to give money to some one, and you're not to."

His eyes twinkled mischievously. " But I will get change—if I have to knock up the treasurer of the church to give it to me—I defy you, magerful woman, I won't be bullied by you." He thumped the table with his fist, and looked so exactly like a naughty child rejoicing in its naughtiness that of course it ended in laughter and the Doctor getting his own way. " I just wanted to leave a trifle for the maid," he explained.

When she came back with the change he was gazing dreamily into the heart of the glowing fire. " Do you know," he began, " I had such a strange dream last night—I think I must tell it to you. I dreamt I was in heaven, and the queer thing was that I didn't feel a bit happier than I had done many a time on earth. There was not a kent face to be seen, and I felt lonely—dreadfully lonely. But just then I noticed a young man by my side, a tall dignified looking man with a friendly open face.

" ' You have just come ? ' he said.

" ' Yes, sir,' I answered.

" ' And are you feeling a little lonely ? '

" ' Well—yes—I was a little lonely ; but since you have spoken to me, that feeling has gone.'

" ' Would you like Me to stay with you ? ' he asked. His eyes were wonderful, as if at some time in His life He had known some great tragedy, and on His brow was the mark of an old wound.

" ' Sir,' I said, ' it is what I would like above everything else, *I feel—I feel as if I had known You all my life.*'

" He stretched out His hand to greet me. There was the mark of an old wound in its palm ; when I looked into His face He was smiling ; and then—then—I knew it—was—the—Lord Himself ! "

.   .   .   .

The old Doctor has passed many years ago. He has entered that Heaven home to which his thoughts went forth while he dwelt among us, and who can doubt that the first to meet and greet him in the new home would be no other than his life-long friend in the old—the tall young man with the scarred brow and nail-pierced hands—the Lord Himself !

THE WEDDING PARTY AND THE DOCTOR

THE " happy couple " had departed, and we, the wedding guests, were left to entertain each other till such time as our various trains and 'buses were due. Most of us were strangers to each other, and the somewhat formal and unhomely air of the hotel drawing-room where we had met certainly did not tend to make us more genial.

I had slipped into a window-seat and was furtively studying a motorists' guide to Perthshire. In imagination I was just negotiating a difficult bend on the Crieff road, when a voice close beside me startled me by saying, " Aren't you the lady who wrote about the Doctor ? "

A tall handsome lady whom I had been admiring from a distance, but whose name I did not know, was preparing to share my window-seat. She had the most charming smile, with just a hint of mischief in it which reminded one of the remark made by Robert Louis Stevenson's father to Fanny, his wife, " I doot ye're a beesom ! " Her next speech proved that this surmise was correct, for she said, with a little ripple of laughter, " He married me ! "

She seemed rather disappointed that I was not more shocked, and presently she went on, " Yes, he married me, and baptised our children, and—and——" She paused, and I knew from her face that her mind was thronging with old, fond, glad memories. " I often wonder at the folks God entrusts children to," she said, with, as it were, a farewell wave to some old, happy recollection. " When I think what an ignorant young mother I was, I wonder my poor little baby didn't die. He used to roar himself red in the face, trying to tell me how much he disapproved of my methods ! I remember one evening he was particularly noisy. He was making

such a row that I never heard the door opening, nor
knew that the Doctor was standing close beside me. He
picked up the young rascal, perched him on his shoulder,
and began marching up and down the nursery floor
with him. The child was so amazed, he broke off in
the middle of a lusty roar, in pure astonishment, and was
so pleased with his new nurse, he never began again.
The Doctor said, ' You're not the first young mother
whom I have taught to hold a baby. You plant the
child right up on your shoulder—but go for your husband. I may as well teach you both when I'm at it.' I
wondered afterwards if the Doctor knew that I was tired,
and whether he took this plan just to get my husband to
do his share of nursing. It would be like him ! He
often used to look in, after that, and I never knew anyone who had such a way with babies. That's the baby
the Doctor taught me how to hold," she said, nodding
laughingly towards a tall young fellow who was standing
near the door.

He looked, one grieves to say, as if he were about to
do a flanking movement to the rear ; but, catching his
mother's eye, he joined her in the window. I could tell
from the way he carried himself that he had been a
soldier.

" I have been telling what a noisy little chap you
used to be, Donald," she said, after introducing us,
" and how the Doctor showed me the proper way to
hold you."

Mother and son exchanged understanding looks.
Then I knew why she was still " a beesom " ; it was
because her boy and herself were chums.

" I can hardly believe you were ever small enough for
anyone to carry you," I said, looking at this young
giant.

" Oh, but he was," his mother said briskly, " and used
to wear frocks and bibs."

" Now, mother ! " the lad protested, " that wasn't
my fault. I can remember quite well how the Doctor
comforted me by telling me I'd be a man before my

mother. It was he who congratulated me on my first pair of knickers (or were they shorts ?)."

"They looked short enough," his mother jeered, "especially from behind !"

Her son affected not to hear, and went on :

"I was only allowed one pocket in those days, and the Doctor put a penny in it."

"Was it a hip pocket ?" I asked curiously.

"How did you guess ?" he laughed. "It was."

"It was about the size of a penny postage stamp," his mother reminded him sweetly. And then we all rocked with laughter.

It was strange how warm and friendly the air of the room had grown. We made a place for Donald to sit down beside us. He seemed to have forgotten he had planned a retreat, and we prepared for "a good old chin wag." The phrase was his, also the complaint that, as his feet were of the "two-feet-one-back-yard" measurement, it was impossible for him to tuck them out of sight.

I liked this Donald from the beginning ; he was such an understanding sort of a boy. And when he spoke, it was to tell of his great school-chum, one Sandy Macleod, who also had been great friends with the Doctor. Both the boys had been in the habit of doing their lessons together ; their homes were side by side. They began Latin the same term, and were not at all sure they liked it. One evening Sandy was grinding up the declensions, when he heard, as he imagined, Donald opening the outer door.

"Come in quietly," he shouted, "wipe your feet, and be quick about it. I'm at my Latin !"

Slowly the door squeaked open, there was the sound of someone wiping his feet with elaborate care, and then—in marched the Doctor !

"I think my boots are quite clean !" he said cheerfully. "I wiped them twelve times. Look !"

Poor Sandy, with a crimson face, was stammering out

apologies which the Doctor brushed aside with, " Let's have a look at the Latin grammar."

A post-card with the Macleod motto, " *Murus aheneus esto*," was lying on the table, and the Doctor read it aloud, with a merry twinkle in his eyes.

" It means," he said, " that the Macleods are a brazen-faced people. Now, the next time I come here, if you attend to your Latin, you'll be able to tell me if my translation is correct."

Sandy always declared that it was the Doctor who gave him his love for Latin, and to this day Sandy's versions are spoken of with respect in his old school. Also, he was able to tell his old friend that the Macleod motto meant, " Be thou a brazen wall ! "

" Where is Sandy now ? " I asked.

Donald looked out of the window for what seemed a long time, and then he said : " In . . . France. You remember . . . Messines . . . June . . . 1917 ? It was then."

*   *   *   *   *   *

Presently he went on :

" You remember the first time *The Doctor* was published ? My folks sent me a copy in the Christmas parcel, and I lent it to Sandy who lent it to another Morayshire ' loon.' Indeed, *The Doctor* went up and down the line all that week, till at last it fell into the hands of Jock Tulloch. Jock was a wild character, but a first-rate soldier. His language, when the Germans began their evening ' strafe,' was so picturesque it received honourable mention from all the rank and file of the British Army ! Yet this particular evening it was noticed he never said a word.

" ' Fit's this you're reading ? ' his nearest neighbour asked, trying to squint over Jock's shoulder.

" Jock glowered dazedly at him like a man wakening out of a deep sleep. Then, after a bit, he cried, ' Oh. man, man, I thocht this hell o' a place was a' a bad dream, an' that I was back again in Elgin, going aff to

play fit-ba' in the Cooper Park.' He began to fasten
his coat more tightly, and to touch aimlessly his rifle.
His voice was a hoarse whisper when he went on :
' It was me that began ma fit-ba' days wi' a syrup tin ;
it was me that made the Doctor break a' the eggs.'
You see, Jock was ' that limb o' Tulloch's ' who played
a match with the old Doctor one famous March morning.
All that night Jock's mind was full of home, and he
spoke again and again of Elgin. In the morning . . .
he went home ; the twin brothers Death and Sleep
carried him there, though a German bullet hit him in the
head. . . . This is queer news for a wedding party,"
Donald said briskly.

An elderly man who looked like a farmer had joined
us by this time.

"You're speaking about the Doctor," he said,
admitting quite frankly that he had been listening.
' Ay, ay, I like to hear his verra name ! He used to
come an' see me when I was in bed wi' a broken leg, an'
whiles he found me ill-natured, an' whiles he found me
real doon-herted, but he aye left me cheery ! One day
he cam' wearin' a braw new tweed suit ; for the most
pairt he wore a stan' o' blacks, an' when he was goin'
awa', says he, ' Ye've never said a wird aboot ma new
claes, James.' 'An',' says I, ' I think they're real
becomin'. Noo that ye mention them yirsell, I must
tell ye sae ; afore I did na like tae.' He took a haud o'
the tails o' the jacket, an' spreadin' them oot says he,
' *Neat-but-not-gaudy*, as the deil said about his new tail.' ' "

By this time the window was getting too small to hold
us, and when tea was fetched in we gathered sociably
round the fire. The table-maid who attended to our
wants seemed to spend an unnecessarily long time over
her duties, and I could not help wondering whether she
was listening to the talk ; for everyone now had some
cherished story to relate.

There was one especially touching one, told by a
quiet-looking lady who was a nurse. She had had a
case of nervous break-down to tend, and perhaps there

" So am I," I said, fumbling for my handkerchief.

All the way home I had the company of the Doctor. " Dead," they say ? " Nay, I cannot think of him as that. Rather does he rest from his labours, but—HIS WORKS DO FOLLOW HIM."

Printed by The Whitefriars Press, Ltd., London and Tonbridge.

MORE ABOUT THE DOCTOR

MORE ABOUT

THE DOCTOR

BY

ISABEL CAMERON

Eleventh Impression

LONDON
THE RELIGIOUS TRACT SOCIETY
4 BOUVERIE STREET, E.C.4

CONTENTS

FOREWORD

An editor once asked me to write a poem. The suggestion so alarmed me, I nearly swooned. The publisher of *The Doctor* has asked me to do something quite as difficult—he has asked me to write a foreword to the new series of sketches. I have bitten the end of my pen, I have gazed at the virgin fairness of the paper in front of me, I have frowned into what artists call "the middle distance," but nothing happened ! Then one suggested that I should at least chronicle my gratitude for the reception *The Doctor* has got, and I can speak now. I do appreciate that—it amazes me, it makes me glad and proud and humble.

When *The Doctor* was first launched on the troubled waters of literature, I prayed that my mere "snow flake on the river" might make an easy and quick port ; that some one might read of this good man and feel helped, but that it should have got the world-wide welcome it has got certainly never entered the heads of any of us who were connected with the launching of this small barque.

The new series is just a handful of stories I have re-told. No one is more conscious of their scrappiness than myself, but perhaps my readers will be charitable, as the original would have been, and will see that there are certain dear, intimate and lovely things I could not set down. All that need be said is that as in life, so in death, he was joyous and unafraid. He entered into the unseen as a conqueror, dying as he had lived, with the high courage which was always his.

There are blithe tales, too, which we would gladly have passed on. Gay stories which show that the Peter Pan spirit ever lived in the Doctor. In all that was lovely and young, he never changed. The years only gave him a riper judgment, a wider sympathy—they never robbed him of his joyous youth.

"Has your mother any pickled missionary for tea?" he once asked a small boy whom I know rather well. "No," said the child, feeling that his mother was rather remiss.

"In all proper manses," the Doctor complained, "one always gets pickled missionary for tea. Did you ever hear of the missionary who was captured by the cannibals? They put him in a cage to make him fat. Day after day passed, and still he was not killed. 'Why don't you kill me?' the missionary inquired. The cannibal chief scratched his head and said apologetically 'We should have done it, I know, but the fact of the matter is—the wife has mislaid the cookery book!'"

An awe-stricken little voice asked, "Did they kill the poor man?"

"Yes, and ate him too! Pass the butter." The Doctor was quite cheerful about the whole matter. There was a pause for just a heart-beat's length of time, and then the room rang with laughter, the old man's and the child's, curiously alike in quality, and heart cried to heart, "It's me—it's me," and the foundations of a glad gay friendship were "well and truly laid."

I had been writing for the *Sunday at Home* for some years, when I got to know the late Rev. Robert Cowan, of the High Church, Elgin. He had retired to Forres, and was available for " supply " ; happy, indeed, the church who got such a " supply."

After he passed away, I wrote a little sketch, " The Doctor's Birthday," which was printed in the *U.F. Record*, and the editor asked for more. " The King's Messenger " appeared in the *Sunday at Home* soon after. A friend of Mr. Cowan said to me one evening, " Why don't you publish those sketches in the form of a booklet, and get it ready for Christmas ? " That was the seed thought of the enterprise ; so our little barque was launched, and has sped to the farthest reaches of the earth.

The new series has been written just as *The Doctor* was written ; a pure labour of love, another stone on the cairn of commemoration.

ISABEL CAMERON
U.F. Manse
HOPEMAN

THE Doctor was visiting the outposts of his parish one spring morning, when he met Bill the Pedlar, whose other name was William Stewart, and between whom and the Doctor there were the happiest relationships.

"Well, Bill, what is in your pack to-day? Pipe organs or grand pianos, or only bagpipes?" asked the Doctor, with twinkling eyes. It was a standing joke between Bill and his customers that he would never admit he had not what was asked for; and his pack held everything from a tie-pin (gold, with diamonds, price twopence) to harvesters' gloves with fingers like hose-pipes.

Bill laughed at the Doctor's sally and swung off his pack. "I have something in the music line, though it's perhaps not exactly what you are mentioning. See to this now!" He handed the Doctor a bundle of songs.

Carefully adjusting his spectacles, the Doctor took the bundle. "But, Bill, these are Gaelic songs! What's the use of showing them to me?"

Bill came from Gairloch in Ross-shire, and his speech held the cunning lilt of mountain burns. A rascal he was, but a winsome reprobate withal, and for such the Doctor had a special fondness.

"Listen, sir, if you please," cried the pedlar. "Here's a beauty of a song. It's called 'The Fairies' Lullaby.' It's all about a poor woman, yonder, who lost her child. The fairies took it and left a changeling creature in the cradle, and though the poor woman looks and looks she never finds the little one. She finds the otter's track, and the swan's flight, and the trail of the morning mist, but not a sight of her darling. Here's another beauty, ' The Mist-covered Mountains.' " Bill threw back his head and sang the first stirring bars of that famous song, " Hail to the Mountains."

> " Hail to the mountains with summits of blue,
>   To the glens with their meadows of sunshine and
>   dew,
>   To the women and men, ever constant and true,
>   Ever ready to welcome me home."

" Fine, fine ! " cried the Doctor, and Bill, now well into his stride, carolled forth a verse of " The Tocherless Lass " to the scandal of a flock of busy crows and the immense delight of his other listener.

" But here is the best of all," Bill said, selecting a leaflet from the bottom of the bundle. " Have you ever heard the psalm tune ' French ' sung in the Gaelic and with the ' putting out of the line ' ? "

Without waiting for a reply, Bill, with incredible flourishes and grace notes, sang the old tune, chanting each line first and then singing the words. There is about the wild rapture of Gaelic singing an appeal to the emotions which it is impossible to describe ; so if the Doctor offered no spoken word of praise, his silence was eloquent, and Bill was well pleased.

" I'm seeing," he said presently, and trying to speak in an everyday tone of voice, " I'm seeing you have Duncan Ross staying here now."

" Yes ? " said the Doctor, encouragingly.   " Do you know him ? "

" Fine that ! Isn't he from Aultbea ? I mind fine when he married. She was a lass from my own place, Gairloch. Kate Maclennan was her name, and Duncan was a ghillie with her father first, and then he got the keeper's place when the old man died. He's pensioned off now, he was telling me, and came here for the sake of getting a house."

Now the Doctor was on his way that very morning to see Duncan Ross, who had come at the last term to a little house near Lagan Burn, the farthest outpost of the parish. Duncan had steadily repulsed all the old minister's overtures of friendship. Polite he had always been, willing to discuss the weather, the price of stock and crop, but nothing more.

He lived alone too, with a weekly visit from a woman to " redd up," which made it more difficult to get " ben " with him. And here this spring morning Dr. Lindsay must needs meet Bill the pedlar, and from that most unlikely quarter get the key to the situation.

" Aye," went on Bill, " when his wife died, the boy was a little fellow, ten or eleven maybe. His father kept him at his lessons, but there was nothing in the boyan's head but music, music, music ! The glen schoolmaster was from Inverness, and didn't he take all the good singers to the Gaelic Mod in Inverness, and who think ye got the first prize for singing but little Alastair ? (He was called Alastair Maclennan after Kate's father.) I never heard the little fellow singing, but I have heard his father Duncan singing in the church on a sacrament Sabbath day, and I just hope the angels may sing as sweet ! ' Coleshill ' was a favourite of his. There's a tenor, yonder, that grips the heart. Duncan would sing it, 'spose it was like this now." Bill closed his eyes and chanted the first lines of the tune. "Then he would swing off into the tenor, and there was one John Macdonald, in the congregation, a grand singer of the bass, and the women would do their part—man—man——" There was evidently no English to do justice to his rapture, and he broke into a flood of Gaelic. "They're telling me," he went on, "that there's churches with organs and fiddles and trash of that kind, but I'm telling you, sir, there's nothing on all the earth like the voices of men and women praising the Lord in the Gaelic tongue to the tune of ' Coleshill ' on a Sabbath day ! "

Poor Bill was away to his boyhood's days, carried thither as only the magic of music can carry us. Since then he had gone to " the far country," but for just a flash he was back to the kirk of his fathers and the glad rapture of the bairn-time. . . . Next minute, he was swinging his pack on his shoulders again, and with eyes which refused to meet the Doctor's, he was facing the road to the town.

"What became of Duncan's boy ? " the Doctor called after him.

Bill turned reluctantly. " Himself and his father did not get on well at all. Alastair went to learn to be a carpenter with David Macintyre, but 'deed, the only thing he ever made was a fiddle for himself. His wages he saved up, and when he had plenty, what did he do but go and buy a stand of bagpipes ? Fifteen pounds, and second-hand at that ; but beauties of pipes, with mother o' pearl inlaid in them and as many as a score of yards of tartan ribbon hanging from the drones and the chanter ! I knew the man in Inverness he bought them from. Well, one Hogmanay-time didn't he go off with some other young lads to the hunting of the white hares, and his father—threw the pipes into the peat fire. . . ."

" Shame ! " said the Doctor warmly.

" It was worse," Bill said. " It was murder."

" And what happened then ? "

" Alastair ran away ; his father and himself had a terrible row, and the laddie went off. Mind, there was no ill in him, only he would not stick to his trade. He let everything go if only he could get music. Some folks say he went to Glasgow, but no one knows, not even his father. Oh, thank you kindly, sir. Indeed I will not be spending it at the Inn. No fears of me," and once more Bill faced the town road.

It was with this moving tale fresh in his mind that the Doctor knocked at Duncan's door. He found the Highlander if possible more aloof and more unapproachable that day than ever. " I wish I could speak Gaelic," the Doctor said, when after a baffling half-hour he rose to take his departure.

" But all your people here are English-speaking," Duncan reminded him.

" You are not, and you are one of my people."

" Oh, I am but a bird of passage here, sir. A solan goose flying northwards, or a lonely swan. Why should you trouble about me ? "

II

By a series of strange happenings, it was autumn ere the Doctor was back in Lagan Burn, and from Peter

Bain, who had a croft next to Duncan's house, he heard that the old gamekeeper was ill and confined to bed. Peter was distressed because the sick man would not allow either himself or his wife to render him the least service. " I want nothing whateffer," he would say politely. " Thank you kindly all the same."

" An' if ye but seen the een o' him," Peter said bitterly, " ye wad ken that *that* wasna true ! He minds me o' a man that's dying o' hunger, no' ordinary hunger, but—but—I think it's hert hunger. D'ye ken if he has ony freens, sir ? "

" Bill the Pedlar says he's an old friend."

" I dinna think muckle o' his freens then ! A drunken auld rascal ! "

" Bill is a great friend of mine."

" Aye, I ken ye're nane perticular either."

The Doctor chuckled. " Well, Peter, I think I must try once more to get Duncan to admit me to his friendship."

" 'Deed, Doctor, ye sudna fash," Peter said warmly. " That Heelanders think ye're no' worth if ye canna speak the Gaelic ! "

Dr. Lindsay was shocked at the change in Duncan's appearance. Always a gaunt man, he seemed now a veritable shadow. His hollow eyes dominated his face, and they seemed to burn as if the spirit behind them were being consumed. There was about him, too, an air of pathetic loneliness which went straight to the Doctor's heart.

Yet the old antagonistic atmosphere was there as strong as ever, and in spite of himself the Doctor felt his spirit chilled. Subject after subject he tried ;

always to be met with the same baffling, polite reply. The man seemed to be ringed round with ice.

"We'll have a word of prayer before I go," the Doctor said. To the Heavenly Father whose presence was always so near him, he spoke now lovingly, confidingly. Did he imagine it, or was there a softer look in Duncan's eyes as he shook hands in farewell?

"Is there anything at all, Duncan, you would like?" he asked, making as it were one more bid for his friendship.

Duncan shook his head. "You cannot give me what I want."

"Perhaps not; but my Father can."

Duncan gave a little shamed laugh. "I am wanting that one would sing to me, in the Gaelic, and to the tune of 'Coleshill,' the 118th Psalm, where it says, 'I in distress called on the Lord.' Now," with a little defiant smile, "can you do that for me?"

A less dauntless man than the Doctor would have gasped at the request. If you think the old minister looked dismayed, you don't know Dr. William Lindsay in the least.

"I'll learn it myself," he cried, with glorious optimism, "or if I cannot I'll get someone who can. *I promise, Duncan!*"

Even Duncan could not help catching some of the brightness of the old man's smile, and returning it wanly. It was the first time he had ever responded even faintly to his visitor.

But outside the door, the brightness fell from the Doctor's face, and he looked troubled. "Father," he whispered, "show me how I'm to keep my promise."

He was still brooding over the problem when he reached the cottage of Robbie Kemp. Robbie, known to the Doctor as a skilful performer on the " cheery wee melodeon," was now grieve to the farmer of Bruntlands, and was married to the girl of his heart (she who had knitted the famous socks whose story is told elsewhere).[1]

As the Doctor opened the garden gate, he was greeted by an outburst of martial music which put the melodeon far into the shade. Wondering much, he cautiously opened the door and peered in. Robbie was sitting on one side of a cosy fire and his wife on the other, and on the table between them was a gramophone, and the music to which they both listened enraptured was the brass band of the Coldstream Guards.

If I were a poet I would sing a pæan of praise in honour of the gramophone, that wonderful treasure which one finds scattered in all sorts of lonely places, bringing happiness and cheer into lives drab and grey enough sometimes ! The Coldstream Guards, however, met with scant courtesy at the hands of Robbie Kemp when he saw who was his visitor. With glad face and outstretched hand he sprang to welcome him, while his wife, a sonsy, kindly-faced girl, laid down her knitting (it was a small sock now for the most wonderful baby in the world, who at the moment lay sucking his thumb and listening to the band), and in a minute the Doctor was in the place of honour and was being asked what tune he would like. " I hae the auld ane that I used to play in the bothy ; d'ye mind on it, sir ? " The eyes of the men met in an understanding look. " I never

[1] " The Doctor Supplies," in *The Doctor*.

telt ony wan yer favourite tune," he said proudly, " but
I hae the record o' it sung by Hairy hissell ! Wad
ye——"

The Doctor laughed wickedly and nodded. In a
minute the kitchen rang with the merry song, and the
listeners joined in the infectious laughter which seemed
to come so magically from the little instrument.

" I canna help lauchin' when I hear Hairy," Robbie
said, wiping the tears from his eyes.

" It's good to laugh," the Doctor said stoutly, for
indeed he had been laughing as helplessly as his host.
" What a fine instrument you have, Robbie ; is it a
new one ? "

" Ma brither Jock, him that's the bobby in Glesca,
sent it at Christmas," Robbie said proudly. " It's the
newest make. I dinna like yon anes wi' the tin horn.
I aye think they sound like a man singin' through his
nose. Here's a bonnie tune noo. Jock's great freen
in Glesca is a Heeland chap, an' the precentor in the
Heelanders' Kirk there. Jock's in his choir, and at
the last Mod this choir got first place for church
singing."

Next minute the kitchen was full of the grave, sweet
melody of the psalm tune " Effingham," a tune well
beloved and full of sacred memories for all the listeners.
It reminded the Doctor of his memorable visit to a
Highland parish at a communion season when David
Macintyre came back from the wilderness.[1]

Robbie, well pleased to do the honours, placed
another record on. " This is a real beauty," he
explained. " I canna mak' oot a wird oo'd—it's

[1] " The King's Messenger," in *The Doctor*.

Gaelic, but ye wad jist ken it's—it's——" He stopped in sudden confusion, this blate musician who had such a keen sense of lovely things

Gaelic music has two sources of inspiration, love and war, and it was of the first of these the new song told.

"Is toigh leam Dia, air son gu'n d'eisd"
(I love the Lord, because my voice).

A voice like a silver trumpet chanted the words, and then the line was sung by a choir invisible, in beautifully balanced and glorious harmony. Then the next line was chanted, and again the others took up the song. The chanter's voice, a clear tenor, could easily be detected swinging off into his own part after chanting the line.

"That's 'Kilmarnock,'" Robbie explained. "There's another tune on the other side. Yes, by the same choir."

"A'm' eigin ghair mi air an Triath,"

chanted the singer. "I in distress called on the Lord" is the translation, a wailing, wistful, haunting melody, and it was sung as befitted the traditions of the old home-land, and the memories which cluster round our solemn Sabbath days, and the tune—I am almost afraid to write it down—the tune was—"Coleshill."

The Doctor was swept by tides of emotion. The Father had not failed him; once more He had kept faith with His servant. The glad wonder of it made his heart swell, so that when the song came to an end, he could not speak a single word.

This was not the first secret the Doctor had shared with Robbie Kemp (the Doctor had a hundred ways of

binding our hearts to his own one), and when he called
at Duncan's house the following evening, Robbie
slipped in after him and took his place in the " ben-end."
He carried beneath his arm a little square box, oh,
quite an innocent-looking box, and in his " oxter
pocket " was the precious record.

Duncan greeted the Doctor with a more friendly
smile than was his wont. How he could have with-
stood him so long was a perfect marvel to the rest
of us !

" And can you be singing the Gaelic psalm already ? "
he asked.

The Doctor's face was that of a child who has a
happy secret. " I said if I could not sing it myself, I
would get someone who could ; wasn't that the
promise ? "

Opening his little Bible, he read the gracious words of
the 118th Psalm, and scarcely had he finished when a
voice like a clarion rang through the little house. Then
the tune of " Coleshill " swept over the listeners like a
cloud of glory.

Duncan started up in bed. Two red spots appeared
in his hollow cheeks. He turned anguished eyes on the
Doctor's face as if to ask an explanation. But the
music mastered him ; he dared not speak !

" I in distress called on the Lord,"

chanted the unseen singer. Stately, beautiful, and
solemn the notes rang out.

" He in a large place did me set,"

the voice went on, after the line had been sung in

glorious harmony. Duncan was listening, his breath coming quick and hurried, and in those hollow, haunted eyes of his there shone " the light that never was on sea or land."

" It's Alastair's voice," he said, speaking in a fearful whisper. " Is himself there ? "

The Doctor hurried Robbie Kemp in to make known to Duncan the plot. " But the voice was Alastair's voice," Duncan repeated. " Wasn't it myself that learnt him yon tune and the tenor of it ? "

The Doctor lifted the record, and putting on his glasses he read the title. " ' Coleshill,' sung by the Glasgow Gaelic Choir ; leader, Alastair Maclennan Ross."

The old gamekeeper's face was quivering piteously, seeing which the Doctor, after somewhat hastily clearing his throat, said : " The Father never does things by halves."

" He's my boy, and I—I—burnt his bagpipes."

" Pooh ! " cried the Doctor. " So long as you didn't boil them and make them into haggis for a Burns' night supper, it doesn't matter ! "

*   *   *   *   *   *

It was Robbie Kemp who wrote to his brother Jock that very night, and who was so glad and proud to have a share in the happy secret ; and when the Doctor next called at Duncan's house he was welcomed and his hand nearly wrung off by a tall young man who looked so like a younger edition of his father there could be no mistaking of him. Alastair Maclennan Ross had come home, and the very thing which had divided father and

son in the old times now united them. " I'm thinking,"
Duncan said as he shook hands, " I'm thinking, sir,
that though you cannot speak the Gaelic with your
tongue, you're understanding it in your heart, and
that's the best of all."

THE DOCTOR'S HOLIDAY

ONE of the ways the Doctor had of making us love him was his unexpectedness. No one could ever foretell what he would do or say next. Companionship with him became a thing of happy surprises.

The particular summer of which I am writing had been hot and rainless, and by August the Doctor was feeling the need of a holiday. One of his old " boys," now a minister in a city charge, offered to come and take his place for a month, an offer the Doctor thankfully accepted. This young friend came on Saturday, and as the Doctor did not go till Monday, it gave him the welcome opportunity, which comes so seldom to a minister, of sitting in his own pew, and listening to a sermon. " You'll pray for rain," were his last words, as they parted at the vestry door. " I'm afraid for the crops."

The Doctor realised, as few do, that it is the folks in the pew who make the man in the pulpit either a success or a failure ; so I need not tell you that the sermon was a memorable one. And in the prayer that followed, the preacher pleaded for refreshing showers for the panting country and the parched crops. The Doctor whispered a great " Amen."

And, as they were coming out of church, there was the welcome patter of rain drops. The earth, as if to show its gratitude, sent up a sweet damp smell, and one could almost see the plants drinking the welcome rain. With great content, but no surprise, the Doctor looked about him as he opened his umbrella. Then he said, in a complaining tone of voice : " I didn't think the Lord was such a respecter of persons ! Here have I been praying for rain for the last month, and no notice taken ! But when a young whipper-snapper from a city church, forsooth, prays for rain, behold an immediate answer ! Ay, and he hasn't even provided himself with an umbrella," he went on, regarding his young friend with merry eyes. " Come and get a share of mine."

Then, very tenderly and very appreciatively, he spoke of the sermon ; golden wine, he called it, the finest of the vintage.

" I'm sorry you preached so well, because all the folks will go home now, and they will come back in the evening and bring all their friends with them, and they will expect as good a sermon as they got just now. Of course, you can't possibly have another as good."

But this young man knew his Doctor !

" It will be quite as good," he said sturdily, "if you will strengthen me by your prayers again."

And the Doctor, a curiously soft light in his eyes, gave him a fatherly pat. A young man after his own heart, this ! One to whom he could safely entrust his congregation.

With his capacity for making and keeping friends the Doctor was no more than five minutes, figuratively speaking, in Janefield, his holiday quarters, when he discovered one of his innumerable family to whom he had been a true father in God. This was a young man who had listened entranced, one March evening, to the Doctor as he preached on " The river clear as crystal," [1]

[1] " The Doctor Supplies," in *The Doctor*.

and who had offered his arm to the tired minister on his homeward way. They had talked astronomy, and the Doctor had delighted the listening lad with his marvellous knowledge of this science. He had sent him a book, too. Little unremembered acts of kindness done, which were now bearing a rich harvest, for John Maclean was preparing to go into the Church. A Tent Mission had been started in Janefield, to which students came month after month and gave of their services. Young knights, they were, as truly as if they rode forth against an armoured foe ; full of enthusiasm for the Captain.

I need not tell you that the Doctor (he had come for a holiday) immediately took his place in the firing-line shoulder to shoulder with John Maclean, giving, with all the splendid generosity of his nature, the riper experiences of his head and heart. Night after night found him in the tent, and a great tide of revival broke over the place ; old Christians, weary by the way, perhaps, were rejuvenated and new souls were born again.

Among the vistors to Janefield was Miss Janet Hunter, a wealthy lady who came every year to the place. " The only thing I possess is money," she told herself bitterly, and even this money had been the means of separating her from the only man she had ever cared for, and who had cared for her. She was proud and rich, he was proud and poor ; a woman's long tongue, dropping a poisonous word here and another there, had done the rest ; and so they parted. It did not make things easier for Janet Hunter to know that the man had gone under—disappeared from all his old haunts.

A sudden shower as she was passing the Mission Tent sent her in for shelter. The absolute sincerity of the Doctor and his friend impressed her in spite of herself, and she listened—at first with curiosity and then with interest.

Next night she was back, and the next too.

On the fifth night she stayed behind, begging for a word from the Doctor. From that interview she went forth with the vision glorious in her eyes, and a new hope in her heart. " I have found the Messiah," she whispered.

Next night she was absent. The following day there was no trace of her, and the Doctor was on the point of seeking her out when a note was handed to him. It was from her, begging for a brief visit.

He found her heavy-eyed and miserable-looking. Her face had the look in it of one who has lost all that makes life possible. A Bible lay on the table beside her ; but it was closed.

" It is all a mistake," she said dully. " I should not have said I had found the Messiah ; it was all a delusion."

She bent her head, great tearing sobs convulsed her frame. The Doctor let the storm spend itself. Then he said, in the most matter-of-fact way :

" Well, it's quite easy to put the matter right ! No need for this anguish ! Just say to yourself that you don't want Him—that you won't look for Him, that you don't like His Book, nor His friends nor His servants, nor His Day. That's all ! "

She gazed at him in blank astonishment.

" But—but—I *couldn't* do that ! " she gasped.

And then the Doctor laughed ; tenderly though.

" My dear," he said, looking at her with his wise, understanding eyes, " don't you understand that all these doubts and fears are just temptations from the pit ? Oh, I know, I've been through the experience ; so had Paul. We're in good company, you see."

He opened the Bible at Hebrews vi., and read from verse 4, ending with verse 9 : " But, beloved, we are persuaded better things of you." And out of those somewhat forbidding verses he preached a sermon which satisfied Janet Hunter's head as well as her heart.

" I'll tell you a dream I had once," he ended. " I dreamt, one Sunday evening—you will notice the devil is always extra busy on that day—I dreamt I was lost and in hell. I went up to one who stood by the door and I asked, ' Where do people go on Sabbath days ? '

" ' We have no such days here.'

" ' Then where do I meet any good people ? '

" He shook his head.

" ' There are no good people here.'

" ' I should like something to read ; I should like a Bible.'

" With that he opened the door wide.

" ' What do you here ? ' he shouted. ' You want the Sabbath Day, the company of saints, the Word of God. *Out of this*—hell is no place for you ! '

" Why," he went on, " did you send for me ? Why do I find a Bible beside you ? Why are you missing the services ? ' But, beloved, we are persuaded better things of you,' and that's the application of my sermon. And we must tell the Father that here are we, a pair of

stupid, wandering bairns, losing ourselves in the fog of
doubt, but longing for the sunshine of His love."

*   *   *   *   *   *

The Tent Mission was coming to an end, and Janet
Hunter, a happy woman now and mindful of the
"ministering to the saints," conceived the idea of
asking all the maid-servants of the various boarding-
houses to come and have tea with her. She asked the
loan of the Mission Tent for the feast, and ordered (from
London, no less !) hampers of cakes and goodies. I
never could understand why she chose those particular
guests ; neither could they, and *not one* of them came,
NOT ONE.

"Experience," Janet Hunter said, with a rueful
little laugh, looking at the prettily laid out tables,
"is getting a comb after you're bald ! What am
I to do with those mountains of cakes and rivers of
tea ? "

The Doctor and John Maclean, who had come to
help, exchanged troubled looks. Outside, in another
corner of the field, a steam organ was blaring forth
with brazen voice, "Sweet Marie," while merry little
folks on prancing steeds with flashing (leather) nostrils
and flowing tails, curvetted madly round the ring.
Bramwell's Famous Menagerie, Circus and Show had
come to the place. From early afternoon till late at
night that terrible steam organ shattered silence into
fragments.

"That's 'God Save the King ! ' " the Doctor said.
"It must be the end of the afternoon performance."

He went and stood for a little in the door, looking

out into the sunshine. The sunshine was in his face as he came back.

"There was Another who made a feast, and the guests all, with one accord, began to make excuses. He sent out to the highways and hedges and gathered a company of guests. Might we do the same? We won't have far to go. I think I can answer for plenty of willing guests. Are you willing, Miss Hunter?"

She was.

The show folks were just getting ready their tea, rather a sketchy affair it seemed, when an old minister, with the friendliest face in the world, came and asked them to have tea in the Mission Tent. They were to be the guests of the lady "next door."

Mr. Bramwell, whose wife had been planning to give him a raw "ingin" with his tea, said he didn't mind, and the gorgeous lady who did tricks on horse-back said she'd prefer something stronger than tea, but seeing as nothing stronger was offered—why, she didn't mind either.

So the Doctor marshalled his queer guests, from the proud owner, who wore a fur-trimmed overcoat and a diamond ring, to Massa Johnson, the "coloured gent," who looked after the piebald horses.

"Is everybody here?"

"Yes, everyone 'cept Joe the clown, who says he's a headache, and has gone to the caravan over there. Proud chap, Joe—keeps hisself to hisself."

I wish I could show you the Doctor and the show folks as they gathered round the table! Before his genial presence every shadow of constraint and embarrassment fled. Yet no one forgot his own place, no one was familiar ; everyone was gloriously happy.

" Gee ! Wot a spread ! " the trapeze gentleman whispered, and, but for the restraining influence of the tight-rope lady, he would have turned a few hand-springs then and there.

The Doctor said grace. And then there was " one crowded hour of glorious life ! " No need to wonder what was to become of the mountains of cakes and rivers of tea ! The show folks solved the problem. The atmosphere of the tent was that of a happy home, with the hungry children gathering round the father's board.

" Not another drop, if *you* please," Mrs. Bramwell said, leaning back in her chair and giving a satisfied sigh ; " I'm full up."

This set the others laughing, and jokes and laughter followed, tongues wagged gaily.

Under cover of the noise the Doctor whispered that there was one guest who had not come, and he told of the clown who had a headache. Miss Hunter, all the soreness of her despised hospitality forgotten, piled a tray with cakes and tea, and made her way to the " Yaller caravan, miss, that one there."

Carefully she climbed the steps and knocked. Rather a cross voice called : " Come in." For a moment she could see nothing. Then from somewhere in the dark-ness came a voice which said, " Please do leave me alone. I'm quite all right ; at least, I shall be by seven o'clock."

Janet never knew how or where she laid down the tray. Her heart was drumming in her ears, her knees

were shaking. There are some things one never forgets
—voices are one.

" *Joe !* " she said—that was all, but she was stretching
out her hands.

There was a hurried movement from out the darkness, and then a man, gaunt, hollow-eyed, but with the
unmistakable stamp of breeding on him, was by her
side. " Janet ! " he breathed hoarsely.

*   *   *   *   *   *

Meantime in the Mission Tent the show folks were
entertaining the Doctor and his friend. Balancing,
conjuring tricks, extraordinary tying of knots, which
straightened out if you blew on them, contortions from
the boneless boy, and even a coon song from Massa
Johnson, who had a voice like velvet !

And then the Doctor opened his Bible and read to
those poor wayfarers the old story of the feast in the
house of Matthew, and of the glad companionship
there. Ah ! How near was the Master as the Doctor
prayed ! Hearts were strangely moved and touched by
the wonder of the love that sought sinners, and called
them to repentance.

One of the greatest of the Doctor's treasures is a
" Pass for self and friends to Bramwell's Famous Circus,
Menagerie, and Show," made out for all time and for
all places wheresoever the show may be, and presented
to him by the proprietor himself.

Whether he ever accepted this offer, and attended the
Circus, is a secret which only Janet Hunter could tell.
She laughs and says, " Don't ask me ; ask Joe."

Now Joe is the name of her husband.

THE DOCTOR AND NAOMI

"**B**UT why do you call the bag 'Naomi'?" Jack asked Dr. Lindsay.

"Because," said the Doctor, "like Naomi, it goes out full and returns empty. Now you're not to look when I open it."

Carefully he set Naomi on the seat of a chair in front of him and opened it a tiny piece. "If anyone *dares* to come at my back and peep in—I'll—I'll eat them up," the Doctor threatened, turning round suddenly to find both Jack and Betty close at his back. He gave a roar of rage, and immediately the bairns scurried back to their seats ; but they were not a bit frightened really ; this was part of the game, part of the ritual of opening Naomi.

From its leather jaws now emerged two beautifully mysterious looking parcels—one for Betty—one for Jack. Betty's was a tea-pot—a "really tea-pot"—full meantime of chocolates, but ready afterwards to do its duty at any tea-party. Only a little girl who is some day to be a happy housekeeper knows the joy o. playing with a tea-pot which really pours out tea. The Doctor—who had a sporting spirit—bravely drank a cup of tea then and there, and the quantity of that harmless beverage which Betty herself drank had to be seen to be believed.

Jack had a knife, with as many as twenty-two (if I remember aright) different things—including a weapon for taking stones out of a horse's shoe (so useful). It was fastened by a chain to the person of its owner, and was altogether a most *scrumptious* thing in knives. Sharp too !—Jack tried its edge on the dining-room table—oh just the *wee'st* little bit—results, most satisfactory, that is from Jack's point of view ; what his mother thought is, of course, another matter.

"Put Naomi up into my bedroom, please," the Doctor said—handing the empty bag to Jack. "Put her in a comfortable place, far from draughts. She's apt to take rheumatism when she's empty."

The Doctor had come to "supply" for Jack's father, a minister, who was ill, and perhaps that was the reason the rest of the household were so preoccupied, no one noticed Jack and Betty holding a series of secret meetings. These began on the stair, as Jack was going up with Naomi in one hand and his precious knife in the other.

"Isn't it a beauty ?" he exulted. "Did you notice the thing for gouging holes in straps ? Just *feel* the little blade,—like a razor." Betty refused this tempting offer. "I say, Jack," she began, "couldn't we put something in Naomi—I was awfully sorry when the Doctor said she always came home empty."

Jack's face kindled—"Oh do let's," he cried "*Hussh*," Betty warned, "come on into the nursery, and let's think."

The result of this secret meeting was many hurried visits to different parts of the house—there was a shaking forth of the pennies in their "Pirlie pigs"— there were mysterious runnings up and down stairs with queer bulges concealed about their persons. Finally, Jack said, "I'll put in my boxie for Naomi. What d'you say, Betty ?"

" The one you were to make the burglar alarm with ? "
He nodded.

" It's quite a good boxie, and I'll carve ' N ' on
it to show who it's for ; I can easily with my new
knife."

Had it not been that the grown-ups were busy with
their own affairs, they would certainly have noticed
the extraordinary behaviour of the children. As it
was, they escaped—and Naomi, quite a plump and
fat person, reposed beneath the dressing-table in the
Doctor's room. The box with the " N " took some
doing, so Jack had to leave it out.

Fate favoured the little conspirators, and when
Monday morning came Jack volunteered to carry
Naomi to the station, in fact he wanted to carry the
Doctor's big bag as well, but of course he was not
allowed. " You carry Naomi," the Doctor said, " and
put her with her back to the engine ; she gets a headache if she faces it."

Just as the train was starting, Jack thrust into the
Doctor's hand the little box. " It's for—for,"—but the
engine shrieked, and for whom the box was intended
was a mystery. The Doctor put the mysterious parcel
into his greatcoat pocket.

Jack drew a breath of absolute relief as the train
steamed away, and the plot was not discovered. At
the next station a gentleman whom the Doctor knew
joined the train. He was carrying a bag the very same
as Naomi, which, without noticing the likeness, he laid
down beside that lady.

Yes, you can guess the rest. When they reached
their destination, this traveller helped the Doctor

out—handed him his *own* little bag—seized Naomi himself, and with a warm handshake hurried away, neither of them noticing the mistake.

James Wallace was always hurrying. That was the great pity of his life. Since his wife had died, leaving him with one little daughter, he had tried to make business fill his empty life. Nellie, a shy, sensitive little mortal, he regarded as more or less of a burden and responsibility. To do him justice, he was so much from home he did not know how lonely the child was, nor how her little heart hungered for love and companionship. This very day, this Monday with which we are concerned—was Nellie's thirteenth birthday, and the question which had been occupying her mind all day was, would her father remember? When she was smaller she used to remind him, and the conscience-stricken way he would rush out and buy her something was touching. But though this was nice, it wasn't the same as if he had remembered himself, and so Nellie resolved not even to hint at the memorable date. Still, when a little girl enters her " teens," it is nice if someone remembers to make a fuss.

She was watching eagerly for her father, and ran to open the door as soon as his hand was on the gate. "Well, little woman," he said, and stopped. There was an eager expectant look in her face, which somehow reminded him of her dead mother, and he stooped and kissed her tenderly, a most unusual thing. "Any letters ? " he asked, next minute. " On my desk ? " " That's a good lassie ; run up with my bag, you can take out the things if you like. Tell Kate to hurry with tea."

Nellie, with Naomi in her hand, ran upstairs. " You can open it," he had said, " and take out the things." He sometimes said that ; Nellie knew he meant her to take out his pyjamas and shaving-tackle.

Still, to-day would perhaps be different. Something told her it was to be different. . . . Yes, it was.

Instead of uninteresting garments and things, here was a lovely white tissue paper parcel, beneath was a box, then came a beautiful untidy, bulgy parcel which smelt sweetly of lavender, and beneath was one of those delicious animals—the dying pig. Everyone knows and loves this beast. When you blow him up, he slowly fades away from before your eyes, and finally, with a groan, he dies. But you can make him live again, which is the joyful part !

With a happy little gasp, and with hands trembling with excitement, Nellie examined the contents of the parcels. The box had chocolates, the hard-hearted kind which use toffee and almonds for hearts ; the bulgy parcel was a lavender pillow, the other parcel was a woolly scarf, and I have told you about the pig !

A little mouse began to run up and down Nellie's throat, but she was happy, happier than she had been for ages. She gathered her treasures all together again, and laying them gently into the bag, she clasped Naomi to her starved little heart, hugging and kissing it as if it had been a baby.

Then, with a lovely flush on her face, and still hugging her presents, she rushed downstairs to thank her father.

" You remembered," she cried, half laughing, half crying, and threw herself into his arms. " I was just hoping and *praying*, Daddy, you would 'member this was my birthday, and you did, and you brought me such lovely, lovely things, oh, Daddy, how kind you are—thank you, thank you," and so the grateful little heart poured itself forth in a very passion of love and thankfulness.

It was lucky for her that her face was hidden in her father's breast, so that she did not see the bewilderment on his.

Like a flash it came to him that he had all unwittingly changed bags with Dr. Lindsay, but oh why had he not remembered ?

"Thirteen, to-day, girlie," he said, after a rapid mental calculation. "Why, you're a young lady now, into your teens."

Shyness, like a disused mantle, had fallen from her, and with starry eyes she looked into his and laughed. It seemed to James Wallace as if he had never known his little daughter, till that moment. How like her mother she was growing, too ! He hugged her close, and they both laughed, and it was thus the Doctor found them.

"It's Nellie's birthday, Dr. Lindsay," Mr. Wallace said.

"And just look at the lovely presents Daddy has brought me," the child cried.

The eyes of the two men met over her head. . . . One could always trust the Doctor to do the right thing ; and the tense pause was noticed only by Mr. Wallace.

"Many happy returns, lassie," the Doctor said, " why didn't I know it was your birthday, too ? "

Naomi gave a sigh of sheer relief, but only her old

master heard it, as he went on, " If you'll run and put your hand in the pocket of my overcoat you'll find a boxie, with ' N ' carved on it. I think it must be meant for you."

When the child left the room, James Wallace made a clean breast of things.

" Perhaps it was just God's way of reminding you of your little lassie," the Doctor said, with his own gracious smile, " I like to think He used those manse bairns to be His messengers—little Jack and Betty are undoubtedly at the bottom of this mystery, yet it's not a mystery after all, it's just the great Father wanting His bairns to be happy. I must write and tell my little friends that they have done a great thing."

" Greater—than—they—can—ever—know,"   James Wallace said with a husky voice.

So Naomi went home empty, after all, yet I cannot think of the little bag, and the gallant part it played that Monday, without remembering also that the things that endure, the lovely things, which are worth while, are the things invisible.

"SUCH PITY"

ONE—TWO—THREE—FOUR ! boomed from the clock in the Muckle Kirk. It was a dark January morning, and the old cathedral town was sleeping cosily abed, except where a wraith-like shadow, stepping stealthily along, or a moving figure behind a blinded window, told of sin and sickness.

John Macmillan, the policeman, whose beat extended from the Manse Road to the Riverside Walk, counted the strokes, then just as the last one died, he became aware of another sound ; a soft opening of a door somewhere in the neighbourhood of the Manse. For all the bulk of him, and the ancient jest about his elephantine tread, John could move swiftly and silently enough when he liked, and in a minute he was close to the garden wall and peering into the gloom beyond.

Yes, the Manse door was open, and out stepped a tall figure. The wan-faced moon which shone fitfully in the sky chose, at that moment, to shine, and John saw that it was indeed the Doctor ; his cap pulled well over his eyes, his coat collar turned up to his ears, and a steadfast, purposeful set in his shoulders, which told more eloquently than words that the old minister was setting out on some especial errand.

The policeman watched him go down the street, and pondered as to his destination. " Where in all the world is the minister going to at this time o' night ? " he asked himself. " Someone must be sick or in trouble."

A sleeping town seems quite different from the same town awake. Ghosts and shadows are everywhere ;

familiar houses and shops, especially shops, take on an unfamiliar aspect. Queer folks are doing a queer marketing at this time, and John, who came from Skye, shivered and turned briskly on his heel.

The Doctor passed down the street, and turned into the station at the foot. A few sleepy porters were standing about, but the place looked eerie ; even the bookstall, usually a bright spot, was sleeping behind its wooden shutters, and in deep shadow. The few lights only made darkness visible, and when the south train glided into the platform it had a somnolent air. From behind the drawn blinds sleepy heads were raised to peer forth to read the name of the station, and to sink to sleep again. They were bound for Inverness, and the regions beyond ; it was well to let them sleep and forget their sorrow !

Only one passenger alighted. From a carriage near the end a young man had stepped out, and after a hurried look about him had slipped into the shadow of the left-luggage room. There was no one meeting him ? Well, it was all right ! He would show folks, his father, for instance, that he wasn't the first, and he wouldn't be the last . . . but how cold it was.

Just then a tall figure swooped down on him, and with smiling face and warm outstretched hand was greeting him. "Hugh, my boy, I couldn't see you at first ! How are you ? Yes, isn't it cold ? Come away at once ! I wanted you to come and have breakfast with me, but your mother wouldn't allow me. She must needs do that ; that's how she's not down meeting you too."

The traveller had no luggage. As they passed under

the light from the station clock, the Doctor stole a glance at his face. There was something so haunted, yet something so pathetically young in the misery of the lad's face, the old minister felt his throat grow suddenly tight.

"How strong the wind is!" he exclaimed. "May I take your arm?" The warm human contact brought the most blessed comfort to the young man, and into his heart, which had been seething with bitterness, there stole the first ray of peace.

Arm in arm they passed out of the station. Peter Macleod, the porter, who was an agnostic (he said so himself) and didn't believe in kirks or ministers, looked after them with a strange soft look in his eyes. "Gosh!" he exclaimed, "the verra sicht o' that minister is as good as a sermon! D'ye see him airm in airm wi' Hugh Burgess, an' him new hame frae the iile?"

All unconscious of this, the Doctor and his companion had turned into the dark street. A doctor's motor flashed towards them, and a voice from the inside of it hailed the minister. "He's gone, Dr. Lindsay, just about half an hour ago. You might look in when you have time and see the poor wife." Then the motor passed on.

The young man clutched his companion's arm. "It's—it's not my father?" he whispered hoarsely.

"Tut, tut," said the Doctor easily, "of course not! Your father is quite well. It's old Mr. Hall, the grocer, who has passed. He had been ill for a long time."

The lad gave a sigh of relief. They were coming near the end of their journey; they could hear the cry of the river as it flowed by, and Hugh's home was by the Riverside.

"How is my mother, sir?" he asked.

"Wonderful! All mothers are wonderful! I think if our Lord had been telling the story of the prodigal's mother instead of his father He would have said, ' The son took his journey into a far country and his mother went after him and took him back ! ' "

"I know my father is angry," the other said ; and then he added bitterly, "the way of transgressors is hard."

"Yes," the Doctor agreed somewhat drily, " and for that they have only themselves to blame. God gave each of us a will and a conscience, and if we choose to follow our own will, and never heed our conscience, then, the way is hard."

Dr. Lindsay was far too skilful a surgeon of sick souls to allow any wound to fester ; he knew that he must deal straightly with Hugh Burgess, and he did. But he did not inflict one unnecessary pang, and very tenderly did he bind up the wound afterwards.

To old Adam Burgess, once farmer of Burnbraes, and the " nesty buddy " of another tale,[1] now living in retirement in Rose Cottage, his son's conduct had brought anguish of soul. Coming as he did, of a long line of self-respecting, God-fearing ancestors, who had looked the whole world in the face, his was an experience which bewildered him, dazed him, and left the very innermost soul of him raw and bleeding. To his dying day, Adam Burgess could never see a policeman without becoming physically sick. Ay, the iron had

[1] " The Doctor Visits," in *The Doctor*.

entered his soul; and it was his only son who had brought this shame upon him! And because "to be wroth with those we love doth work like madness in the brain," the old man's steady, relentless, unforgiving attitude towards Hugh had often driven the Doctor in desperation from the house. Be sure he did not leave the matter there. But God's time had not come yet, and what sort of reception the son was to get when he reached the home he had clouded no one could tell.

At the corner of the street they cannoned into the policeman, who gave a satisfied grunt, and just before they turned up the Riverside they saw, standing in a ribbon of yellow light, the figure of a blue-cloaked nurse. " Don't let anyone disturb them," she was saying; " and I'll be round about nine o'clock to bath the baby."

There was a small smile on the Doctor's face as he listened, and then he quoted, " ' Only winds and rivers, life and death.' Another little ship launched on the sea of life. God keep it safe ! "

They had almost reached Rose Cottage when a shadow detached itself from the other shadows about the gate, and with a passionate cry of " *Hughie !* " his mother had flung herself into her son's arms. The Doctor turned his back on mother and son, and became absorbed in watching the morning star which was beating and pulsing whitely in the sky. . . . He had reached now the most difficult part of his mission and, like his Master, he had need of a few moments of quiet prayer.

He must have got assurance that all was to be well, for his face, when he turned it to them, was serene.

"A cup of tea, please," he said in the most everyday fashion. "Come along, Hugh."

A cosy meal was laid out in the sitting-room, and a bright fire was blazing on the hearth. Yet there was a tense emotional strain in the little house, which the Doctor sensed; much was at stake. "Father, give me wisdom," he breathed. He knew that the door of the bedroom, opening off the sitting-room, was slightly ajar; he knew, though how he knew he did not know, that Adam Burgess was behind that door, and that he was watching, with relentless eyes, the whole scene.

Hugh and his mother, still clinging to each other, sat down on the sofa near the window, and exchanged glances. No man can sin and suffer alone, and Hugh Burgess learned that bitter lesson as he looked at his mother. He had left her comely, fair-haired, and middle-aged; he found her now a little old, old woman, with a face sad beyond all telling, and with trembling hands and head.

"Oh, mother, mother, what have I done to you," he sobbed, throwing his arms round her. "You mustn't love me like that—I'm not worth it!"

"Hush, hush, Hughie," she whispered, fondly stroking his closely cropped hair. "You are."

The watcher in the room beyond gave a little gasp, which only one person heard, and that person said, after a little pause, "Are we or are we not to get something to eat?"

"Oh, forgive me, Doctor," Mrs. Burgess said, wiping her eyes and coming to the table with a very April face "Come, Hughie, sit down, my dear."

" We'll ask God's blessing," the Doctor said, and knelt down. So did the others, their hands close clasped.

The Fatherhood of God was always, as I have said before, the supreme thing with the Doctor ; perhaps it was the secret of his own happy inner life. In the prayer which he offered up, he dwelt upon this beloved theme. " *Like as a Father pitieth His children, so the Lord pitieth them that fear Him, Thine anger endureth but for a moment, Who is a God like unto Thee, that pardoneth iniquity . . . because Thou delightest in mercy . . . Thou— Who spared not Thine own Son . . .*" There are some things of which it is not lawful to speak—this was one of them. . . .

Let me say, however, that long before he reached the " Amen " another worshipper had joined the little band, and was kneeling, his body shaken with sobs, close by the Doctor's chair. And out of the darkness and the desolation of the night came One like unto the Son of God, the unseen Guest, who came not as a wayfaring man who tarries for only a night, but as one who comes to abide, and that for evermore.

*   *   *   *   *   *

Hugh Burgess calls his sheep farm in Australia after the old home farm. He is doing well ; a somewhat silent, shy man, one whose word is seldom heard. But ask any wild young fellow, who has suddenly pulled up, and is doing better, ask him about Hugh Burgess, and you will hear a tale that will warm your heart.

He keeps a bundle of letters inside his Bible. In

one cherished and oft-read letter in the Doctor's large
and spacious hand he reads :

" Your father has joined our Young Men's Fellowship Guild. I asked him to pray the other Sunday
morning, and he prayed for you. At least what he
said was ' For those whom we carry in our hearts night
and day, but who are separated from us by lands and
seas, we crave a Sabbath Day's blessing.' If the name
of the person your father carries in his heart all the
time and prays for all the time is not *Hugh*, then I
don't know what it is ! He must stop praying in such
moving fashion ; I felt that in another moment the
tears which filled my eyes might fall and I would be
shamed before all my young men ! "

Very tenderly Hugh puts this precious letter back
into its place, which is in the Book of Psalms, close by
that wonderful psalm which says, " *Like as a father
pitieth his children, so the Lord pitieth them that fear Him.*"
Through the love and forgiveness of his earthly father
he has groped his way to the love of his heavenly
Father—who has " such pity."

M.D.   D

THE WIND UPON THE HEATH

"Life is sweet, brother : there's day and night,
brother, both sweet things : sun, moon and
stars, brother, all sweet things : there's likewise
the wind upon the heath."

—Borrow.

"HOO are ye a' the day?" Johan, the Lady of the
Dish Basket, stood smiling, with arms akimbo, her
basket already established on the door-step. Johan
meant business.

"It's a fine day, Johan, but I'm not needing any
dishes," I answered hurriedly. The pan of jelly I had
left on the kitchen range was at the critical stage when
anything might happen.

Johan laughed tolerantly. "I'm gled ye think it a
fine day ! Some micht think it a wee saft," and then,
abashed, I noticed that it was indeed raining steadily.
"I wis speirin' wis ye a' weel," Johan went on, "It's a
lang time since I seen ye ! "

Johan had the most wonderfully infectious smile,
and in spite of my unwillingness I had to respond—
and was lost !

"Come in and tell me where you have been," I said,
and led the way, somewhat hurriedly, to the kitchen,
just in time to prevent the apple jelly from turning
itself into toffee.

"Ye didna see onything aboot me in the papers ? "
Johan asked anxiously. She had a modest dislike of
paper publicity.

She swung her heavy basket beneath the table as

easily as if it had been a feather. She was a tall, strongly-built woman, about fifty, with something big and spacious about her, a creature of the open, with the long swinging stride of a hill dweller. Folks said her father had been a laird's piper, and Johan had inherited his step (though not, alas, his name!). There was something about her which always hinted at tragedy ; she had been born for great things but not for happy ones. In her younger days she must have been a bonny lass, with her debonair air, her flashing brown eyes, white teeth and wavy black hair. To her husband, Isaac Williamson, a weasel-faced little wisp of a man, with trustless eyes, she was blindly devoted. It has been hinted that he was not her first husband, nor even her second ; Johan never did things by halves. About her matrimonial arrangements she was wonderfully silent. Upon Isaac she lavished all the mother-love she would have given her bairns if she had had any, and her dutiful wifely love as well.

"Ye hevna seen ma name in the papers since Februar'," she said proudly, " an' then it wis only a breach o' the peace ! "

She listened to my congratulations with a modest smile. " A' ma freens is pleased," she said, " Mrs. Wood an' a'. Aye, she's a rale leddy—mony's the time she's taen me hame on her airm, when I wis—drunk."

Johan was no hypocrite ; her honesty disarmed criticism. " I've gien that up noo," she went on eagerly. " I hevna tasted since Februar', an' then I couldna," she smiled whimsically. " I wis a' that month in the jile, an' ye maun be sober there ! "

" At the back o' the New Year," she went on,

" Isaac selt his powny an' we went on the spree. I canna keep sober in yon toon," she cried passionately. " There's pubs. an' bars at every corner an' fowk ready tae tempt ye, speshully if they think ye hae twa three bawbees. If ye dinna drink, ye'll see them nudgin' ane an' ither an' winkin' at yer back an' makin' a fool o' ye ! When that happens, I tak' siccan a drought in ma verra hert that only a dram can cure it ! I'm a marked wumman in Gileston, I'm tellin' ye ! The bobbies a' ken me, an' watch me ! Weel, I wis walkin' doon the street an' I met that cock-eyed, wooden-legged scoundrel o' a Robbie White—the man that aye leads Isaac astray, an' says he wi' a nesty fleering lauch an' a wink, ' Weel Johan, are ye sober yet ? ' an' says I," she paused and looked at me apologetically " Sure's deth, mistress, this wis a' I did." She put her two hands tandem fashion (shall we say ?) the thumb of her left hand bearing somewhat firmly on the tip of her nose, causing that feature to become almost violently retroussé, then she uttered, with the most roguish twinkle in her eye, the magic word " *Toor-il-oo !* "

" That wis a' " she cried. " Yon dowg o' a bobbie— ye'll mebbe no' ken the Gileston bobbies ?—weel it wis yon reid-headed tod—they ca' him ' Red Geordie,' he couped me ! They planned the thing, him an' Robbie White, an' it wis ' *Johan Williamson up again, breach o' the peace.*' Thirty days ! "

Johan could tell a tale with dramatic power, and the way in which she mimicked the various voices and actions in this somewhat sordid little drama, was too much for my gravity. Seeing which, Johan girded herself up for fresh efforts.

"A breach o' the peace is no' siccan a bad thing as being cruel tae a bairn or a dowg, or being drunk or— or " her eyes grew merry, " slappin' a bobby's fat cheeks ! That's a awfa' sin ! Thirty days an' *no option !* Whiles—whiles I think it's worth it—it's siccan a satisfaction, speshully if it's yon Red Geordie ! " A wicked jade, this Johan, but no one can deny she had a diverting way with her !

"Are ye no' for ony dishes the day ? " she suddenly asked ; after all, business was business ! " Bowls, puddin' dishes, cheena cups, a crystal rose bowl— they're all the rage noo ! Here's a beauty, cut crystal ! "

" Oh, Johan," I said reproachfully.

" Weel, they telt me it was crystal," she fenced. So we left it at that.

" What is that yellow dish—that one wrapped in paper ? " I asked. She dived into the basket, and laid upon the table, as tenderly as if it had been a baby, one of the most biliously yellow jugs I have ever seen. Elephants and tigers, all the same size, frolicked round it. The elephants (you knew them by their tusks) were evidently pursuing the tigers, a fact which these amiable animals seemed to find vastly entertaining. They wore frills round their necks—or perhaps they were whiskers ?

" A jungle scene," I said in my best " company " voice. Something complimentary was evidently expected of me. But if I thought thus to parley with Johan and truth, I soon found my mistake.

" No, nor a jungle scene," she snorted angrily. " That's a puckle kiln cracks ye're lookin' at. I wadna sell that jug for a hunner punds," she went on.

"That's good," I replied drily.

Johan's eyes flashed, and my heart smote me. After all, tastes differ.

"I meant those animals, those elephants and tigers, Johan." Her temper died down as quickly as it sprang up.

"Oh, that bastes! That's coos an' horses—the kind they hae in far-off places like France an' China." After which statement there seemed nothing more to be said.

To cover a somewhat awkward pause, I offered and she accepted a taste of my apple jelly. Johan was as fond of sweet things as a child. While she disposed of the "jelly piece," she told me the story of the jug.

When Johan was in jail she had evidently done some thinking. If she were to keep straight, then she must leave the town. Isaac might not be willing; but she was the chief bread winner, and she meant to have her own way. With the "wind upon the heath" blowing clean and sweet, life would be an easier thing than in the squalid little room with its hateful smells of rags, rabbit skins and other abominations. She had not spent all her money ere she was "couped," and she knew where a pony and a cart could be got cheap. Then with a tent, a basket of dishes, the "heaven above and the road below," life would become a high adventure.

Isaac was not very willing. He was troubled with a mysterious complaint known as "a tumult in his inside," and the only medicine that could cure him was a dram. Johan took her own way of dealing with the situation. She went into no particulars as to her method.

The weather that March was wonderfully good, and the open life restored Johan's health, and steadied her nerves. She was passionately fond of nature, and a happy song was often on her lips as she swung along from farm-house to farm-house, jesting, bargaining, laughing and joking, and then returning to the tent at night and the sweet companionship of " Moon and stars, brother, and the wind upon the heath." Oh, life was good again !

The day of days wherein Johan had her wonderful adventure was a Sabbath afternoon. She knew the day, because the ploughmen were not working in the fields, and into the little schoolhouse at Earn Brae decorous country folk, clad in their best clothes, had gathered for a Sunday service. Isaac had gone to " see a man aboot a horse " always a good excuse, and Johan was alone.

It had been raining, and the wind was full of the gracious scents of glad spring. Birch trees made the air sweet, the pungent odour of burning whins hung over the moor, and by the burn-side bog myrtle buds were bursting into leaf, and if there is a scent in the whole world to match this I should like to know its name !

The brown burn was telling itself secrets as it chuckled past, laughing at the complaining notes of the muir fowl who were wailing overhead. In a clump of last year heather an adventurous bee was searching for honey. Oh, a glad glamorous world, all clean and new ! A wave of longing swept over Johan as she stepped along, water-pail in hand. If only she could be made new and clean again, get another chance like the moor, how wonderful that would be ! The wind upon the heath had stirred her strangely ; the ache of unshed tears was behind her eyes. Whiles—whiles she feared this " drought " would get the better of her !

When she reached the spring she was surprised to see an old man sitting on the bank. By his dress she knew he was a minister ; she eyed him doubtfully. The meeting in the school was evidently over.

The minister returned her look, but with so much friendliness in his expression, Johan, always responsive to kindness, felt her heart warming towards him. " I was wanting a drink," he began, " but the water is so far down I cannot reach it. Would you——? " He paused and smiled at her. " Would she—aye ! Mair than that," she assured him, and with swift feet she flew back to the tent to get the yellow jug. It was the best she had—she wished passionately it had been gold !

Carefully she lowered the pail and then filled the jug with water clear and cold, with the magic and the mystery of the moor in it.

The old minister thanked her, and then taking off his hat, he closed his eyes. Johan had once seen and heard a Salvationist praying at a street corner in Inverness. He had shouted as if his God were far off. The God this old minister prayed to must be very near, for though she listened eagerly, she could catch no word.

" What's so good as water when you are thirsty ? " he said, as with a gracious smile he handed her back the jug.

" I wish it wad slocken my thirst," she answered

wistfully. " I hevna tasted a drop o' whisky since Februar', but whiles the drought is gey bad." How it happened she never knew, but in a moment she was telling him all about her life, and Johan was no hypo-crite, she told an unvarnished tale. He listened sympathetically and did not seem shocked, only sorrowful, and once he murmured softly, " Poor soul."

Was there a chance for her? she asked, and he told her that where sin abounded, grace did there much more abound. He read to her, too, the sweetest story she had ever heard, of another woman at a well, and of the wonderful happenings which followed that meeting ; of the water of life which could quench all thirsts, and so make her new again. Then he had knelt and prayed, but it was exactly as if he had been talking to some near Friend, to whom he committed Johan and all that was a care and a burden to her. " He telt me," Johan said, " that if I prayed tae Him, He wad tak' the drought outen ma hert, an' I did, an' He's doin' it," and so she ended a tale which left me rather silent.

" That must have been Dr. Lindsay from Gileston," I said, presently.

" Aye, he wis waitin' for his freens tae come wi' a motor tae tak' him hame." She lifted the yellow jug and put it back in her basket. " Ye ken noo why I like it ? " she said.

" And the Doctor ? "

Her face quivered. " I—I—jist canna—speak—aboot—him—bit—gin—I—could—do—onything ! "

* * * * * *

From the Doctor himself I heard the rest of the tale.

He had been deeply impressed by Johan's personality, by her amazing honesty and humility, and by her anxiety to learn. "I had been tired after the service," he confessed, "the folks at the meeting had all enjoyed an excellent dinner and were sleepy and unresponsive, so you can understand how Johan's keen, living interest refreshed and helped me. Did you ever know, by the way, that Isaac thrashes her? Well, he does; she told me, however, that if it pleased him it did her no harm. All the same, I'm going to have a word with Isaac on the subject." From this and another remark, I gathered that the Doctor knew more of Johan's affairs than any one else.

Christmas week brought Johan to my back door. "Where are you camping just now?" I asked, and she told me, in a voice which forbade questions, that they were back in the town. Over a cup of tea she became more expansive. There was a pained look in her eyes which reminded me of a dog that had been ill-used. The "powny" had died, Isaac's "tumult" had grown worse, and so she had been forced to return to the squalid slum life with all its degrading environments. "But I'm keepin' richt," she assured me, and I knew it was true, "an' I'm savin' ma bawbees tae buy another powny." She smiled wistfully. "I'm keepin' ma money in the yalla jug. I see the Doctor often, an' he prays for me, an' I ken the Lord will gie mair heed tae him than tae me."

When she rose to go I noticed for the first time that she had some difficulty in lifting the basket of dishes. "No, it wasna too heavy, bit—bit—she had hurt her side—oh it wis naething." There was something about

Johan that day I shall never forget, a gravity, a sweetness, and a certain aloofness which were memorable. It was with the greatest difficulty I persuaded her to accept her train fare to Gileston. "You must not dream of walking seven miles, Johan, and your side hurting you." She turned away her head, and I saw her eyes were full of tears.

"Good-bye," she said huskily, "and thank you kindly." I watched her go out at the gate. Her "piper's" step had gone, she dragged herself along the road.

When she returned to her stuffy room that evening, Isaac was out. She had left him ill in bed. She went to a neighbour's house, and was told that Robbie White had been out and in all day, and that finally the two had gone out, "lauchin' an' jokin'." Like a stricken animal, Johan rushed back to her room. The "hidie hole" where she had kept the yellow jug was empty, the jug itself, smashed into fifty pieces, lay under the bed, and its contents, which had meant so much to her, the "wind upon the heath, sun, moon, and stars, day and night" were gone—gone to supply a drunken husband and his bottle companion.

*　　*　　*　　*　　*　　*

Presently she went out, no one knew where. Isaac, staggering home drunk and penniless, threw himself on the bed. It was supposed that he had put his lighted pipe in his pocket, and that that had set the bed clothes on fire. Johan, at some nameless hour, returning from her Gethsemane, found the room full of smoke. Blindly she groped her way to the bed and tried to lift the sleeping man ; but the weight of him was too much, and she fell beneath it, fell among the ruins of the yellow jug, cutting her head and hands on its broken fragments.

From out of his drunken stupor Isaac slowly returned to consciousness, and stumbled forth to a place of safety, leaving Johan bleeding to death. It was by a queer irony of fate that Robbie White found her. They carried her to the hospital, and kind hands did all in their power to alleviate her sufferings. It was then it was discovered she had a terrible bruise on her left side. "This has been done some time ago," the nurse said. Johan, who had so often covered Isaac's ill deeds, could do so no longer ; for she lay unconscious, a broken wreck, on the little hospital bed. Then from immeasurable distances and desolations, her soul came shuddering back to its earthly tabernacle, and she opened bewildered eyes, and asked where was she. She asked for the Doctor, and he came. "I'm going," she whispered, "*Is—is—it—all—richt ?*"

"It is all right, Johan. You have fought a good fight, you have kept the faith." Then he read to her her favourite story in the fourth chapter of John's gospel.

"That wife did mair nor me," she whispered, "she telt the men o' the city, an' I never even telt Isaac. Whaur's Isaac ? " she asked suddenly, anxiously, the old protective love still strong in her. "Tell them no' tae jile Isaac," she pleaded, "he's a puir craitur an' disna ken better."

Exhausted, she lay back and asked that the window might be opened wide, "I love the win'," she said, and for her once more the wind was on the heath, and she was back in the camp at Earn Brae. By the well side there sat a man, a young man, tired and weary looking. "Give me to drink," he pleaded, and she had taken the yellow jug (it was all new and mended) and had filled it full. When he stretched out his hand for it, she noticed blood trickling from a wound in the palm.

"Your hand is sair?" she asked.

"An old hurt," he replied. "It sometimes bleeds but you have made it better."

"I didna—do—onything," she faltered.

"You said '*Forgive*,' and '*He knew not.*'"

Johan recovered consciousness towards evening, and whispered to the Doctor her vision. It was but a passing flicker. She gazed for a moment intently, as if into the unseen; a strange light shone in her eyes. She whispered softly—amazedly, "There He is—that's Him—the man I gaed the water to"—a pause and then a lower whisper, "*He's kind*—oh, *He's kind*," and so she passed.

THE DOCTOR AND HIS EDITOR

WHEN my friends are confessing my sins for me, which they do with quite unnecessary frequency, they always draw special attention to my untidiness. "Just look at the way you keep your cupboards," they will say, "especially that one by the window. Why, no one can open it without getting an avalanche of letters poured forth."

"No one has any right to open that cupboard," I retort angrily, "and besides they are all letters about the Doctor. I simply cannot burn them."

Still nursing a feeling of resentment I opened the cupboard door and let the Niagara of letters fall into my lap. Sitting on the floor I made up my mind to sort them into two heaps, these on my right to be kept, these on the left to be burned.

The first letter I opened must have been written in 1915; there is no date (it's from a woman, who puts 'Wednesday' at the top) and underneath is the name of a Nursing Home. Because she met "the Doctor" there, and because he helped and cheered her and made her forget her burdens, she writes me a little note in pencil (for which she asks pardon) "One of the nurses lent me the book," she writes. "She said it would make me laugh and cry. It has done both, and it has given an uplift to my soul."

Clearly I cannot burn this letter.

The next is dated 12th January, in a man's firm hand-writing, and it comes from a southern city. There is a coat-of-arms upon the envelope; that, and the embossed address and the quality of the note-paper would tell anyone without being in the least like Sherlock Holmes, that the writer is someone of consequence. Yet he says " I have loved reading your book so much I am sending it to a number of friends in England. I envy you the authorship of the Doctor." A nice man this unknown correspondent, to love my Doctor. Presently he goes on to say " If there should be another edition, you might correct the punctuation of the metrical psalm in ' The Doctor Visits.' "

There was another edition, and I did correct the punctuation, and I now take this opportunity of thanking my unknown friend. It would be discourteous to burn this letter.

Next comes one from Toronto, written in July. It begins with " To the Authoress of the Doctor " and the name at the end is hard to decipher. However, " the Doctor " has brought great joy to an old lady whose forbears came from Scotland, and as the book was light to hold, she could read it in bed. She wished to thank the writer, and to say that while loving all the stories, she loved especially " Davy's Dog." As I happen to know Davy and his dog rather well, I decided to keep this letter too.

Here is a refreshing letter. It begins straight away, " Pardon an old woman's inquisitiveness, but will you tell me is the Doctor a real person ? In any case accept my grateful thanks for introducing me to him."

The address is St. Andrews. Cautious warm-hearted Fife ! She goes on to tell me that her son bought the book for her, *having first read it himself*. I like that mother and son ! I wonder does he always censor her reading for her ? Anyway I must not burn this letter.

There is no doubt what I am to do with my next letter. It must be kept if I have to get a cupboard built for itself. The date is written in precise Roman numerals (things I can never understand) and the writer addresses me as " Dear Sir." He calls " the Doctor " a booklet and writes to point out the many errors which it contains. Who read the proofs, he wonders ; some grossly inaccurate person. Page, paragraph, and line are duly noted, *there are ten of them*—though there may be more which he has over-looked. He suggests that the writer should add a vocabulary for the benefit of English readers. He fears that even some Scottish folks may find a few words difficult to understand. (My poor country !) What, now, does a " limb " mean and what sort of an animal is " a clockin' hen ? " There are actually two dozen words full of mystery which he advises me to explain. He asks me—(how unnecessary)—what is " a nesty buddy ? " He adds, however, in quite a kindly way, that if I carry out these improvements the booklet will be quite a pleasant one and leave a clean taste in the mouth.

Having put this letter in a careful place, I take up the next which comes from a Yorkshire vicarage. The Vicar, an understanding man, does not ask me is the Doctor a real person. " I know and love your Doctor," he writes. " He reminds me of an old vicar I had whom I loved when I was a curate," and he goes on to tell me of the death of his friend—a beautiful story ; too sacred to be set down here. After reading this letter I had to pause a little to rummage for my ever elusive handkerchief.

Following this is a letter from one who knew the Doctor in the days of his flesh. It is dated 1918, and asks that more stories may be added to a book which " is a gem of purest ray serene." " I knew the Doctor," he goes on to say, " and received many kindnesses from him." The address at the top of this letter is " House of Commons," and alas ! before the enlarged edition was ready, this kind writer had passed on ; probably has discussed the stories with the Doctor by this time, too ! It would be sacrilege to burn this dear letter.

My next letter is from Sussex, and the name is not that of a lady but of a gentleman, who begins fussily (that's what made me think my correspondent was of my own sex), " Do excuse me asking questions at such a time. Is the chapter ' Davy's Dog ' history ? A friend to whom I sent the book ' shied ' at this story and said it spoiled the whole thing." I remember trying to reassure this doubting Thomas (he enclosed a stamped envelope) ; for Davy's Dog is still an exceedingly healthy, hefty animal who disputes the ownership of the study hearth-rug with the lawful owner, and groans if you so much as give him the wee'st of pokes !

Canada sends me a greeting, a breezy delightful letter it is too, with a Highland signature. It warms my heart, and so dear, unknown clansman, I wave you a warm message, and keep your letter.

From Drogheda, Ireland, is the next letter. A Presbyterian minister finds time amid many duties to write and thank me for a book which has " captured " him, and he signs himself " Yours indebtedly." I have always had a warm corner in my heart for Ireland. I shall keep this letter.

My publisher, with whom I share many queer epistles, sent me one which has made me rock with laughter many a time. "Sir," this letter begins, and you can see that even the writer's pen was spluttering with wrath—"Having seen your advertisement for a book called *The Doctor*, and thinking it might contain some simple prescriptions for chilblains, chapped hands and such like, I sent for a copy for my nephew, who is a soldier. When the book came, I find it is by way of being a religious pamphlet *and absolutely no use !* Please return me my money. I would suggest that you get the author to change the title for something less mis-leading." He adds, as an afterthought, "If you have any really good book at the same price, you can send it to me instead of the money."

As I read this letter once more, my eyes met those of the Doctor from his place on the mantelpiece, and I solemnly declare he was laughing ; I am sure he wanted to know what "really good little book" this man got for his shilling.

"Asker, Christiania, Norway," is the address at the top of my next letter, and it comes from a Norwegian lady who had been interested in *The Doctor*, when the stories first appeared in the *Sunday at Home*. "What a dear splendid man he must have been," she writes in her beautiful careful handwriting, and she goes on to tell me how much she would like to translate the book into her own mother tongue, so that her own country folks "might know and be the better of knowing this wonderful personality." It gave me—it still gives me—queer thrills to think of the Doctor making his way among a strange people, yet not strange either, for the Doctor's gospel is a universal one.

From Elgin, town of happy memories, comes a gem of a letter. It was written by a dish-hawker, who, all honour to him! is fighting a stiff battle in one of Elgin's slums. The very surroundings of his home must make it doubly hard to follow the gleam. " I really don't know how to express my grateful thanks, as I got little schooling when I was young," he writes, in beautiful copperplate hand, very thin as regards the up-strokes and very fat as regards the down-strokes ! He tells me in words which, if somewhat originally spelled, cannot hide his meaning, that the story which helped him most was the one about the Young Man with the scarred hands and the wonderful smile. I knew from others how well and bravely this poor man is fighting on, and it did cheer me to be told by him that " Your book was like a sunbeam from heaven, and made me happy, for I knew the Tall Young Man was the same Christ Who said ' Lo, I am with you always.' "

It is a proof of the greatness of the Doctor himself that a message should be sent from a Roman Catholic Abbey in Wales. " I cannot resist writing to tell you how much I enjoyed reading *The Doctor*, especially ' The King's Messenger.' I am sending for some more copies to give away." From a Baptist Manse in the same country comes a similar message. " All one in Christ Jesus," the Doctor would say.

" I take off my hat to *The Doctor*," is how the next letter begins, " and to you as having revealed him

for our encouragement." The writer is a young Civil
Servant in India, whose first name is David and whose
mother (she has just passed) loved " David Macintyre." [1]
He notes, too, that Macintyre means " The son of the
carpenter." How glad I am someone has at last
noticed that David's name was so apt. The beautiful
Gaelic meaning has at last been revealed. Burn this
David's letter ?——

It was on a Monday morning the next letter arrived !
I remember it well ! " Himsell " was in bed, being
weary with his " fighting with wild beasts at Ephesus "
the preceding Sunday, and I raced up the stair to read
him this wonderful letter, and found when I sat down
on the foot of the bed I couldn't after all ! That this
great man should write me and should say such words
about the Doctor—well I would that my tongue could
utter the thoughts that arose in me. But it could not,
and after all it was " Himsell " who read the letter,
and laughed at me ! The " Sclater's House " [2] was the
story this great man loved best, and he spoke generous
words about all the stories, and he told me how the
book held him from the first page to the last. This is a
letter I shall bequeath to my grandchildren, if I ever
possess any !

A London minister writes to ask where can he get
the tune " Effingham," the bass of which is so wonderful. He is sending copies of *The Doctor* to his class of
young students. " It is better than any text book," he
says. What of that man who said he couldn't understand what a " limb " was or a " nesty buddy " ? I

---

[1] " The King's Messenger," in *The Doctor*.
[2] " The Doctor Visits," in *The Doctor*.

wonder how those London students got over the difficulty.

A blind lady who has had such a happy time with the Doctor, gets her secretary to write and ask permission to put the book into Braille. I can imagine the Doctor's pleasure, and how he would murmur " I am come to bring sight to the blind," and he would glorify his Father.

Another correspondent wonders can I be the lady he once met in Nova Scotia. He rebukes me for using " The Maister and the Bairns," [1] as if it were my own writing. No, I certainly did not meet this person either in Nova Scotia or any other where. But I sit rebuked about the poem. Inverted commas were not enough. This is the reason why in the eleventh edition there is a note as to the authorship of this lovely poem.

And so the pile grows ; how can it be otherwise when every letter has something different to tell me ? This, for instance, with its homesick, wistful note which comes from New Guinea, and has been wandering from Australia to New Zealand and thence to Scotland and Elgin from some lonely keeper of an outpost, and the Doctor has come to tell him " All's well." Another, with the ominous words " C—— Sanatorium," at the top, tells of a patient who is getting better, but still sleeps on the verandah, or rather lies on the verandah, and when he cannot sleep the Doctor keeps him company, and he quoted " And with the watcher a watch he keeps," [2] and tells me how the words have helped him.

[1] " The King's Messenger," in *The Doctor.*
[2] " The Doctor Visits," in *The Doctor.*

Another who calls himself " a dweller in the tents of Kedar," but whose post-mark is an African town, and who has come originally from Inverness, writes to rebuke me for the way I have spelled or rather mis-spelled some Gaelic words. The idea ! Didn't " Him-sell " edit my Gaelic at the time ? However, I forgive this unknown friend, because he tells me that the communion at Gorry Glen has been a great experience for him, " for didn't I know everyone that was there from Sutherland, the dour elder to Rory who drove the mail gig ? "

I have kept the good wine to the last. It comes to me from across the Atlantic where so many of my countrymen have welcomed the Doctor. The writer of this letter had gone for a holiday to some country place beyond Toronto. One Sunday afternoon he had gone for a walk. He noticed a man doing something to a sickly-looking tree, and he stood watching him. Finally, he began to speak, as is the friendly way of that land.

" Where do you came from ? " he asked the forester.

" From the Island of Lewis."

" And your name is——? "

" Cameron, sir."

" I have a little book in my pocket which a writer belonging to your clan has written about a great and good man. Would you like to read it ? "

" Thank you kindly, sir," said the man politely. His voice lacked enthusiasm, however. Books about great men did not interest him. Then, with the Highland courtesy of his old home, he asked the stranger would he like to come and see his friends ;

there were two of them, and they shared a shack just a little way off.

Strangely enough, both the other men came from the Western Hebrides too, one from Harris and one from Skye. They received the stranger politely, but there was no disguising the fact that they were not prepared for visitors. The shack was untidy and so were the men. No, they had not been in church. Sunday to them was a day for loafing about. Oh, no, they had not been brought up like that; Cameron, the first man, had had a godly father who was an elder in the Free Church, and Mackenzie, the red-headed, blue-eyed young giant who came from Harris, had had a godly upbringing too, " and both my parents were members of the church," he added, and told how his mother had been frightened to come forward because she was not worthy, and of how the old minister had told the diffident fearful soul " ' Merran ' says he, ' *It's for sinners—it's for sinners*,' and so my mother was always coming forward after that," he added, with a beautiful simplicity. The youngest member of the shack had joined the others only in April, and he had not managed to get work. He was from Skye, and his name was Donald Macleod.

" What could he do? " the visitor asked, and then and there he held, as it were, a committee meeting with himself and decided that just such a lad as Donald was needed in his store in Toronto. But this was not Sabbath news, was it? So, promising to return next Sunday, he left them.

Cameron met him at the shack door the following Sunday, and he wore his best clothes, and there was a look in his eyes which had not been there the previous week. The shack was spotlessly tidy, and on the table lay a Bible, *The Doctor*, and writing material. Presently the other two men came in, and they also were in their Sunday clothes.

The very atmosphere of the shack seemed changed. "We thought you would like to hear we have all been in church to-day." It was Cameron, the tender of sick trees, who volunteered this information. " Twice," he added.

Mackenzie, after a little silence, tense with emotion, said huskily, " We're taking the Books after this " (that means they were to have family worship). Their vistor nodded. At great moments words seem useless things, besides—— . . .

Donald Macleod's soft voice, sweet with the lilt of the Highlands, said quietly, " Myself, I was writing home the day. I—I was not writing them since a long time. I could not get work and—and I was not liking to be writing them, but now, now that you are giving me the chance of a job, and after reading about what that little bookie is saying of the lads in the bothy at Burnside writing to the home folks, I put home word, and I'll do it every week regular after this."

*　　*　　*　　*　　*　　*

The three men accompanied their visitor to his home. None of them referred to *The Doctor*, but in parting, after clearing his throat once or twice, Cameron, as being the most experienced, spoke.

" We're thanking you, sir, for yon bookie, and my blessings be on you for giving it to us—an'—an'— we're thanking the Lord for *The Doctor*."

And so the Doctor, not like a wayfaring man who turns aside for only a night, but the honoured guest who has come to abide, has made another place for himself, and the fellowship in that Canadian shack is very dear to God.

Only the other day a curiously phrased letter reached me from Canada, and the signature at the end was Cameron. The writer " taking the liberty of thanking you for a precious message, would be most obliged if you would be telling me the name of the tune the cattleman played on his melodeon yon night when the Doctor took shelter in the bothy."

I wave my hand to you, fellow clansman, but wasn't the name of that tune to be a secret ?

So I take up the right hand heap of letters (there are none on my left) and bind them all tenderly with a rubber band, and lay them gently on the top shelf once more. The Doctor, who has been watching me, laughs and says with his wise chuckle, " I thought so."

THE AFTERGLOW

MORE than a decade has passed since the Doctor
has left us, yet when we gathered together on a
certain Monday evening last December, as one of the
speakers so happily put it, " We had still the afterglow
of that grand and great life," and in its warmth we
glimpsed anew the friend we had thought dead.

> " He is not dead, this friend ; not dead
> But on some road, by mortals' tread
> Got some few trifling steps ahead,
> And nearer to the end ;
> So that you, too, once past the bend,
> Shall meet again, as face to face, this friend
> You fancy dead."

The previous Sunday a memorial tablet and a
baptismal font had been unveiled and dedicated to the
" belovéd pastor," and great, ever-to-be-remembered
words had been spoken by one peculiarly fitted for
the task ; but still, like children who have returned to
the old home, memories, fragrant, glad, and tender
held us with wistful hands, and we could not go away.
So once more we lighted the hearth flame, drew the
chairs around it and told and listened to tales of him
we loved. We reminded each other of this tale and
that other. Because there were so many of us, we met
in the hall of the Church, and it was for mere handiness
—nothing more—that the speakers were placed on the
platform. There was a row of men—*and of ministers !*
There was one woman—that was I. If any one has
ever doubted my love for the Doctor let them recall

how that evening I sat in awful solitude, " cannon to right of me, cannon to left of me," and, what should really have alarmed me most—" Himsell " seated beneath the platform. He would, I knew, on our homeward journey, patiently point out all the mistakes I had made—still, to be associated with the " Doctor " on this night of Commemoration, was an honour I shall never forget, and I now record my gratitude.

The hall was crowded, for besides the folks we saw, there was the " cloud of witnesses." Ghosts ! Why, the place was full of them, so that, as one said, the faces he saw most distinctly, the voices he heard most clearly, were those that had gone—but were not dead. And the spirit of the Doctor was there ; in its sunshine we rejoiced.

One speaker asked, how could one harbour thoughts uncharitable, remembering the graciousness and the humanity of the Doctor ? A certain man " righteous overmuch " had insisted upon confronting an evil doer with his misdeeds, and that in the presence of the Doctor, who had, all unknown to himself, been hurt by the man's conduct. He listened to the tale, and then shaking his head, he said with his lovely, tolerant smile, " Tut tut, that wasn't evil doing—it was only *stupid blundering*," and in the charity of his judgment the culprit melted into tears of repentance and another soul was won for God.

One of the Doctor's " old boys " spoke ; he is himself a doctor of divinity ; but as he told the tale of his young days, he was a laddie again. We liked him all the better because his voice shook just a little over the old memories. Once when the Doctor had been presented with a pulpit robe, he had recalled the story of a certain monk who had said he would always hang his habit on a sunbeam. "'I shall hang my new robe on the sunbeam of my people's charity,'" the Doctor had said. "No man less needed the charity of his congregation, for he appeared before them Sabbath after Sabbath, with the truth new minted from the treasury." Then he told of the Bible Class.

Like the Doctor himself, it was unique. One Sunday he set the class hunting for the "wiles of the devil." He could count a whole dozen; could any of the class do better? It was a challenge taken up by two of the lads, and the following Sunday they appeared with a list of wiles numbering twenty! Not without honest pride in this result, they handed the paper to the Doctor who received it with apparent gratitude. "It is evident," he said slyly, "that my young friends are better acquainted with the wiles of the wicked one than I am," and a gale of laughter shook the class.

So, like a jewel of many facets, the stories showed the Doctor in the manifold sides of his character.

Sunday's speaker's stories had a peculiar interest, for he had been the "one and only" colleague the Doctor had ever had.

The relationship between them had been of the happiest and most intimate description. The love between the old man and the young was like that of Paul and Timothy, and the memory was wholly gladsome. "I remember," the speaker said, "how the Doctor took me visiting, for the first time. We went to see an old lady, one of the oldest ladies in the congregation, and, at the Doctor's request, I engaged in prayer. It is not always an easy exercise, though no presence could have been kindlier or more sympathetic than my senior colleague's. I referred to the lady as ' Thine agéd servant '—feeling that that at least was a safe expression. On coming out he asked me if he might give me a little bit of advice. ' It's this,' he said solemnly, ' never refer to a woman's age—never ! God knows it, and He'll forgive you, *but the woman never will.*' And," added the speaker ruefully, as we shook with laughter, " that lady was ninety years old ! "

This speaker touched on a point which has always interested me—that was the Doctor's ability in the midst of laughter (and be sure it was always happiest laughter !) to turn to God in prayer. For him there was no distinction between sacred things and common ones.

" Sacred things were the home where his spirit continually dwelt," and one, at least, of his listeners recalled gay words of the Doctor's concerning a certain new blouse which had come to her one Saturday evening, and how, after the banter and the laughter, the Doctor had dropped on his knees to give thanks to God for " earthly love which binds husband and wife, parent and child, brother and sister." [1]

And then we were laughing again at the way the Doctor *would* go into houses without ringing bells or knocking knockers—and we heard a new and wonderful story of how once the Doctor, mistaking a certain door, found himself in a strange house. He was no wise upset over this, but so much could not be said for the

[1] " The Doctor Supplies " in *The Doctor.*

man of the house, who was a Roman Catholic. Over the mantelpiece hung a picture of the Madonna, and pointing to it, this man said, " We worship her ; she was a wonderful woman." " She was," the Doctor agreed, " *And hadn't she a wonderful Son ?* "

" The most difficult people to live with are one's neighbours," the next speaker told us, but he could honestly say the Doctor had been a most delightful one ; that was the angle from which he showed us our friend. " He was no stickler for formality, and we liked him all the better for it," and then he told us how the Doctor always left sunshine behind him. " He came to cheer you up, to give you something, to invite you to lunch, or to go for a drive, to tell you of some piece of work you had done well, or to tell you ' his latest.' "

One of his co-presbyters had happy memories to recall. There was a great Communion service in his church, where the Doctor took for his theme, " The Suffering Saviour," and preached a sermon which has its influence to this day.

It was also on this occasion an old lady said to him, " I hear they are collecting money to send you to the Promised Land." The Doctor looked solemn and said, " I hope they are collecting enough to get a return ticket—for I don't think I'm ready to stay there yet."

The Doctor as " supply " was the next facet in our jewel ; on this subject I was chosen to speak. Well, the tale has been told in " The Doctor Supplies "—and that afternoon (this tale is told in " The Doctor and his Editor ") rather a wonderful letter had reached me from Canada. It was my privilege to say once more—"He is not dead, he rests, his works do follow him."

Another of the "old boys" took up the tale. His were memories of happy boyhood days, and of how the Doctor had influenced the young by his clear, convincing doctrines. But his practices spoke more convincingly than his doctrine! He had been at a funeral one day; it was that of a poor working man, the father of a young family. The eldest child, a mere laddie, was sobbing his young heart out in the cemetery as the grave closed on his father's coffin.

The Doctor, with tears in his own eyes, stood silently by the stricken boy, and then, with a tender arm round his shoulder, he thrust into the boy's hands all the money he had in his pocket, saying in a husky voice, "Take this home to your mother, my boy." Doctrines? Yes, but who could help loving a man with such practices?

The testimony of the Doctor's own son gave us the closest and most intimate touch of all. It was hard for him to speak; but it was his proud privilege too, and we listened entranced to his words.

And so the tales went round, and it was time to say good-bye, and we found, like the Queen of Sheba, that the half had not been told.

The full tale only he himself can tell, as tell he shall at the final reckoning. "Lord, thy pound hath gained—," and he shall hear the Master's "Well done."

Printed by The Whitefriars Press Ltd.
London and Tonbridge

THE DOCTOR CALLS AGAIN

THE DOCTOR CALLS AGAIN

BY

ISABEL CAMERON

Third Impression
(25th Thousand)

LONDON
THE RELIGIOUS TRACT SOCIETY
4 BOUVERIE STREET, E.C.4

Made in Great Britain

CONTENTS

CROSSING THE MINCH

" I answered : ' You seem so disappointed that I was
not prostrate with sickness you'd almost make me believe
I haven't crossed the Minch at all.' "—THE DOCTOR.

I

A GUST of March wind tore the Doctor's hat off his
head and sent it careering wildly down River Drive
to come to rest at last on the doorstep of No. 10.

To the Doctor a door was always something to be
pushed open. Bells and knockers he ignored. His
friends knew this and loved and welcomed him. If it
sometimes happened that he pushed open unknown
doors he never admitted that it was a mistake. Rather
did he make it an occasion to add yet another friend to
his already long list.

When, on this particular afternoon, he captured his
hat he also found himself in a somewhat dark and over-
warm book-lined room. He was (outwardly, at least)
quite unperturbed. Even when he met the coldly
polite eyes and raised eyebrows of a strange man sitting
in a wheeled chair midway between the fire and the
window he took it in the most matter-of-fact fashion.

He had a primrose in his buttonhole, and something
of the joy and hopefulness of spring seemed to enter
with him and to make the invalid check a longing sigh
which had risen unbidden to his lips. All the same an
Englishman's house is his castle—what business had this
old minister to come in upon him so unceremoniously ?

The Doctor still held in his hand his runaway hat ;
a gleam of pale sunshine entering through the heavy
curtains shone on his white hair ; it lighted on his

brown friendly eyes and it thawed out of the atmosphere
a certain chilly edge and made one think of the coming
summer.

" I beg your pardon, sir, for this most unceremonious
entrance," the Doctor began courteously, " but a blast
of wind sent my hat into your door and left me hatless
and breathless. I confess I thought this was No. 8. I
wonder if you would allow an old man to sit for a
minute or two just to recapture his breath ? The wind
made me feel old, though "—here he chuckled—" I
defy any March wind to make me feel infirm. Like the
devil, I am old—but not infirm."

Certainly no one looking at him would ever call him
either old or infirm. Mr. Purcell's eyes behind his eye-
glasses were watchful but polite. He discouraged
visitors, ministerial ones most of all. Even the best of
them he found took upon themselves to ask him intimate
questions on his spiritual state. They wanted to read
and pray with him ; they wished him to prepare to
meet his God and hinted that he hadn't too much time.
He had told his last such visitor that he did not believe
in God. The remembrance of the man's scared face
made him smile bitterly even yet. It was quite possible
that his present caller belonged to the band of over-
zealous priests and that this friendly air of his might be
a mere excuse for taking an unfair advantage of his
physical state.

The book he had been reading he laid face down-
wards on the table beside him, and then he nodded
politely but stiffly towards an easy-chair at the fireside.

" Pray take a seat," he said. " I am sorry the wind
has used you so badly."

" I don't know that it has," the Doctor laughed,

sitting down and holding his chilled hands to the blaze. " I think it has been very kind to me, blowing me into this delightful room and comfortable chair and giving me the pleasure of meeting you."

This time his smile met with a response. The afternoon was decidedly warmer.

" What a glorious collection of books you have got," the Doctor went on, putting on his glasses. It was a speech to win any scholar's heart. It is almost as good as praising a child to its mother.

" Books are my only friends," Mr. Purcell said.

If he hoped to provoke the Doctor to improve the occasion he hoped in vain, for what he said was : " It's not every man who has so many." He peered at the titles. He went round the room, taking down a book here and another there, but always replacing them, much to their owner's relief.

" I see you are interested in philosophy," the Doctor said. " So am I."

He took down another book which bore the name of an eminent scholar.

" I haven't this one, but I have all his earlier works. It's too bad that scholars' books are so expensive."

Mr. Purcell smiled politely. He was cut off from so much that made life worth living, he told himself, he was perfectly right to buy and keep for his own use all the books he cared for. He hoped this strange visitor would not embarrass them both by asking the loan of a book.

He had seen Dr. Lindsay as he went on his rounds and knew him for the well-beloved minister he was—still, he did not feel inclined to share his book friends with him.

All unconscious of these thoughts the Doctor went

on looking at the books until at last he had completed his circle of inspection and was standing beside the wheeled chair. Mr. Purcell winced ; he feared his visitor was going to refer to his lameness. It was something which had to be borne, but any reference to it made him shrink.

He need not have feared the Doctor hurting his feelings. Taking the primrose out of his buttonhole he handed it to the invalid saying : " The very first this year. I found it hiding behind a clump of withered ferns. It minded me of my bairn days. For two pins I'd have gone off on a whin-burning expedition. The pity was no one offered me those pins."

" Lucky for me," said Mr. Purcell, taking the flower and looking into its innocent, wondering face ; then he smelled it and " Memory woke with all her busy train." How he longed for his bairn days—for the feel of the clean spring air in his face instead of the warm used-up air he breathed day after day. He made a tentative grab at the heavy curtains as if he wished to admit the spring sunshine.

The Doctor was examining the book which lay face downward. Then he put it back on the table, and though his voice said nothing, there was a longing look in his eyes which declared he would like to read it.

Mr. Purcell, stifling an impulse he had not felt for years, began to speak of German metaphysics—a subject upon which the Doctor was well qualified to speak, for to the end of his days he was always a scholar.

For a whole hour time stood still while the scholars discussed, argued, agreed, and disagreed on a subject of mutual interest.

The clock announcing the hour of five brought the

talk to a sudden ending. The Doctor lifted his hat. " That gust of March wind is accountable for this," he cried in dismay.

" I shall always be grateful to it," the other said. " Your visit has been a pleasure." He paused and eyed the book which he knew the Doctor had wished to borrow. Should he offer it ? His head said no, his heart yes.

One regrets to record that his head carried the day.

" May I hope you'll find time to come and see me some other day ? " he said (he'd think over this book-lending matter).

" I shall come with pleasure," the Doctor said in his friendly voice, " and I'll bring those books which you haven't read. I think you'll enjoy them. Shall we say Thursday ? And may I know your name ? You are English, I think ? "

" Any day will suit me," Mr. Purcell said rather sadly and glanced at the rug covering his strengthless legs, and then he told him his name was John Purcell and that he was an Oxford man.

" I shall look forward to my visit," the Doctor said, " and I'm very grateful for your kindness to me this afternoon."

Before Mr. Purcell could reply the Doctor was gone, taking with him the sunshine of the day but leaving behind him, as he always did, a brighter, happier atmosphere.

For long after he had gone the other brooded over his visitor. The Doctor's parting words had been so generous ! He had not waited to be asked for a loan of a book—he had offered not one book but two ! And he had promised to come again. He had not made the remotest reference to Mr. Purcell's state either physical or spiritual, and he had left him the primrose. He lifted the flower and sniffed it. It had lost some of its freshness but none of its fragrance. Again he sniffed and the Recording Angel wrote down that spring was on its way to No. 10 River Drive, and that Dr. Lindsay, the King's Messenger, had been at work, having as his allies a gust of March wind and an early primrose.

II

Had any one told Mr. Purcell that he would look forward with eager anticipation to a visit from a minister he would have raised incredulous eyebrows. Yet on the Thursday of the Doctor's promised visit he had propelled his chair quite near the bay window out of which he could see both up and down the street.

He had ordered his housekeeper, Mrs. Watt, to pull back the heavy curtains which kept out the sunshine. When she had hinted that they kept out the draughts he appeared not to hear.

March was going out like the proverbial lamb and the sunny street was full of boys and girls playing. The boys were flying kites ; the girls dancing through skipping ropes, and their happy voices made music which was good to hear. The wire-haired terrier from No. 7 was pretending an ancient boot was a rat which he must worry, and the cat from No. 5 sat sunning herself on the window-sill looking insolent and bored, turn about. The spirit of spring was abroad, and in the little front gardens crocuses and snowdrops were preparing to depart in favour of golden trumpeted daffodils and fragrant wallflowers.

Mr. Purcell noted all this in a subconscious fashion while looking for the Doctor. Too early yet, he supposed. He took up a new book which had come only that morning and began to read it. But his attention wandered. His eyes were oftener on the street than on the page. He turned a leaf—took another long look up and down—the clock announced it was four. His heart became heavy and told him that probably the Doctor had forgotten—he had so many visits to pay. Ah, well, it was a good thing Mr. Purcell could always depend upon his book friends. They never failed him. He tried, not very successfully, to stifle this newly wakened desire for a human friend. Why, even Mrs. Watt seemed to have a visitor ; he could hear animated voices in the basement and once a sound as of laughter.

He smiled sardonically, remembering that he had made up his mind to lend his book on German philosophy to the Doctor. He wouldn't need to do this now. That, at least, was satisfactory ; he turned to his reading again.

The meaning of the printed word was either very obscure or his mind wasn't working properly, for he could not grasp its significance. He set himself to re-read the page—and then in the queer way we all know but cannot explain he was aware that he was no longer alone.

He lifted his eyes and looked round. There, sitting where he had sat the previous week, beaming on him with all the old friendliness, was the Doctor. He had a couple of books in his one hand and a prim little bunch of spring flowers in the other.

He nodded gaily. " I came in by the back door to-day," he announced. " You see, the folks in No. 8 belong to my Church, and their boy Roddy has to spend his days in a shelter. I have been sitting with the little chap and he has been trying to teach me how to make a kite. By the way, your housekeeper has been very helpful in the matter of making paste for the kite." He gave a little pawky smile. " You were so intent on your book I did not like to disturb you and to say ' How are you ? ' " The Doctor advanced with outstretched hand waiting for an answer to his question, which with him was never a conventional one.

When Mr. Purcell had assured him he was " Fairly well, though not sleeping well," an admission he never made to any one else, the Doctor handed him the books he had brought, and the flowers. " Roddy sent these," he announced casually, " I was looking for a third book, but I think I must have given the loan of it to someone else," he explained. " This bulge in my pocket is made by *Robinson Crusoe*. Roddy and I are reading it."

" The kite-maker ? "

The Doctor nodded. " The kite-maker is the pluckiest little chap you ever saw. Only seven and fated to lie on his back in an outside shelter. . . . "

He paused, as if some things were too pitiful to tell. " Only seven," he repeated.

" This street seems to specialise in chronics," Mr. Purcell said, and if there was bitterness in his voice the Doctor did not hear it.

" Oh, my worst case is No. 6," he said cheerfully. " Old John Mill, a chronic . . . grumbler ! A terrible disease ! I was telling him this very afternoon after listening to his complaints that I had a strange dream about him the other night. I thought he and I had both died and gone to heaven. I met him in the street wearing his crown at a rakish angle and carrying his harp. I said, ' No complaints now, John ? ' He laid his harp carefully on the Golden Street, put up his two hands to his head and removed his crown. 'Do you ca' that a fit?' he asked angrily. 'Seven and a quarter is what they gave me and I only tak' a seven!'"

Mr. Purcell had told himself that he had forgotten the way to laugh; well, he had not, and the discovery did him good. The ice binding his heart gave a great rending crack, and the atmosphere of the room became genial.

Of all the delightsome short cuts to friendship, is there a happier one than that of laughter? The Doctor, well pleased at the flattering reception of his joke, went on to tell him about Roddy's kite, which refused to fly or to wag its tail.

"I fancy the foundation isn't properly made," Mr. Purcell said. "I used to be rather good at kite-making. Everything depends on having the foundation properly made."

"Yes," the Doctor mused aloud:

> "The hert's aye the pairt aye
> That maks a' richt or wrang,"

and then he disappeared.

He was back in a twink, carrying a small and badly made kite in his hand. "Um—m-m-m-m," said Mr. Purcell, eyeing it critically. "Spinal curvature and a high shoulder. May I have it? Rather a pathetic attempt, isn't it?"

The Doctor handed him the kite and watched with keen interest the deft way in which the man handled it. "Would the youngster mind if I just stripped off the paper and got the foundation straight?" he asked. The fascination of creating something was on him now, bringing light to his eyes and youth to his face.

D.C.A.   B

"I'll answer for Roddy," the Doctor assured him. "Man, do you know I never could get the two shoulders of a kite to look the same. Yes, I see how you've done it—you've the mathematical eye." Perhaps he saw in the fashioning of the child's kite that a lonely soul was tired of walking in desert places and longed for human kinship once more.

"You'll get a pot of paste in the bottom of that cupboard," Mr. Purcell said. "It may not be equal to Mrs. Watt's, but it will do." He laughed again. "Thank you. Pass me that newspaper, please."

When I tell you the newspaper so recklessly sacrificed for Roddy's kite was *The Times* of that very day and was still unread, you will understand something of the miracle that was happening in the front sitting-room of No. 10 River Drive.

He had meant to discuss German metaphysics with the Doctor. Instead he found himself instructing him in the making of a tail for a kite. It was the happiest afternoon he had spent for years, and when the clock announced the hour (which was so late one cannot tell it) they were both amazed but pleased. The result of their joint labours amply satisfied them, and as for the excited child he wanted to go to sleep quick, quick, so that the morning would come soon and he'd send up into the blue sky this wonderful kite with its "waggish" tail !

"Will you take this with you, Doctor Lindsay ?" Mr. Purcell asked, handing him the book which the Doctor had looked at longingly on his first visit. No one knew better than the Doctor how to accept a kindness, often a more difficult thing than to bestow one.

"I'll bring it back next Thursday," he promised.

" Metaphysics can wait, but Roddy's kite could not."

Mr. Purcell forgot that he had dreaded the Doctor asking him inconvenient questions. He took a diary from the table beside him, looked at the date for next Thursday, and set a red mark against it ; a small but significant act.

III

The friendship thus happily begun grew with the passing weeks. Every Thursday Mr. Purcell looked for the Doctor ; not once did he look in vain. It is only a " shut-in " who knows what this means.

The Doctor came into that quiet dull room bringing with him sunshine and a hint of summer breezes. There was healing in his presence, and the other, so badly hurt in the battle of life, found his hurts strangely soothed and life assuming more normal values.

The Doctor never entered without a gay greeting ; he never came empty-handed ; there were gifts of friendship in his eyes ; there was kindness in his hands ; generally there was a book in his pocket too.

He never discussed religion or made inquiries as to the other's spiritual state. Long ago Mr. Purcell's anxiety on this point had been lulled to rest.

" I feel," he said one Thursday, smiling back at the Doctor, " that when you come down the street the band is playing and there are flags waving from every window."

Like a mischievous child the Doctor slowly turned round before him.

" Please take notice of my new summer splendour," he laughed. " I'm wearing a new jacket. ' It's neat—but not gaudy,' as the devil said about his new tail."

B 2

" You seem to be on very friendly terms with his Satanic majesty."

" Not friendly, but frequent," he corrected. " He has plagued me for seventy years. I've tried to frighten him all that time and he's not afraid of me yet. Why, at two o'clock this morning he tried hard to make me believe that I was badly used because I couldn't sleep. He said he wondered my Father afflicted me like this. I very nearly believed him too, until I remembered my sleeplessness was my own fault. I took a cup of tea at supper-time instead of my usual glass of milk."

Mr. Purcell's eyebrows were his most expressive feature ; he raised them questioningly and asked : " Do you believe in a personal devil ? "

" As firmly as I believe in a personal Saviour."

A constrained look stole over Mr. Purcell's face. He loved and respected the Doctor too much to hurt his feelings by showing him that he considered such a belief absurd. As a matter of mere courtesy he must make some polite remark.

" Such a belief must be a great comfort," he said.

" I could not face life without it ; I could not face death without it. Only in a personal Saviour can I find rest for my soul."

There was such absolute conviction in the Doctor's words that, in spite all his head told him, Mr. Purcell found his heart crying out for this rest too. For years he had been tossed about " with many a conflict, many a doubt." He had resolutely shut the door on these, but he knew they lived still ; given a chance they would clamour for a hearing.

" I was brought up in the Church of England," he began, speaking with a certain amount of difficulty.

" I used to repeat like a parrot the Apostles' Creed. When we came to the part ' Jesus Christ crucified under Pontius Pilate and buried . . . rose again from the dead on the third day, and ascended into Heaven,' I began to wonder was it true. Oxford at that time was swept by a wave of materialism—agnosticism. How did we *know* He rose again ? How did we *know* there is a life beyond the grave ? No one has ever come back to tell us—we may be living in a fool's paradise."

The smile on the Doctor's face was wholly reassuring and not in the least shocked. " *He* came back," he said softly. " Our Lord Himself—the same old Friend—there was no change. He loved His friends—cared for them as in the days of His flesh. He had a special meeting with Peter who denied Him, and who needed more than the others to be assured that there was no change. Isn't that enough for us ? " Then in his voice which was capable of such wonderful inflections he quoted :

" I know not where His islands lift
    Their fronded palms in air,
I only know, I cannot drift
    Beyond His love and care."

Mr. Purcell looked out at the window. The aloof look which he so often used as armour was absent from his face. " I find it difficult to believe," he said.

The quiet room became filled with voiceless currents of prayer, and an urgent S.O.S. winged its way to God. " Help me, Father," whispered the King's Messenger. " Guide me."

Presently he began : " When I was younger I once went to help a fellow minister at a Communion season.

He lived in Stornoway, in the Island of Lewis. It meant crossing the Minch. There isn't a worse piece of water round the British Isles than the Minch. I'm not a good sailor, and I confess with shame I dreaded the crossing.

"I got on board full of apprehension. The crossing the previous day had been bad—a choppy sea and a contrary wind kept the boat late. We all expected the same. Well, the sea was like a mill-pond, there wasn't a breath of wind—we got into Stornoway in record time. My friend was waiting for me with an anxious face. 'What sort of crossing had you? Were you very sick?'

"'I was neither sick nor sorry,' I answered. 'I enjoyed every moment of the sail.'

"Mr. MacLeod looked at me in blank amazement and repeated : 'You weren't sick !'

"I answered : 'You seem so disappointed that I was not prostrate with sickness; you'd almost have me believe that *I haven't crossed the Minch at all*.'"

Mr. Purcell's eyes were fixed on the Doctor's face. He could read the hidden meaning of the significant story. The person of Christ was always to the Doctor a subject of endless delight, and he preached that Christ now. Not a God who was far off but a homely Christ —tired, hungry, sad, glad, craving human sympathy, lonely at the end, with a cry wrung from His lips that has no equal in all history. He tasted death for all men —He made it easy for us to cross the Minch. He went alone through the darkness of the night, but He comes with us when we have to cross. "Forgive me if I have preached—you know I did not mean to."

"I wanted you to," Mr. Purcell said, and April, with its showers and sunshine, with its promise of

flowers and fruit, was in the room, and a soul was
" asking his way to Zion with his face turned thither-
ward."

IV

The summer was a hot and rainless one. There was
much sickness in the town. The little kite-maker in
No. 8 had no longer any interest in his kite. There was
no wind to send it skyward. Languid and listless he
lay in his shelter ; even the adventures of Robinson
Crusoe had ceased to interest him.

But one Thursday the Doctor found him full of life.
" The sick man in No. 10 sent me this," he said.
" And it has the loveliest pictures." He held up for the
Doctor to see a big book. The Doctor adjusted his
glasses and read the title. One cannot truthfully say
it was a book suitable for a seven-year-old. It was a
learned treatise on Egypt, but the pictures—and there
were crowds of them—glowed with colour and fascinated
the child. Mr. Purcell had never lent a book to a child
before ; in fact, until he knew the Doctor he had never
lent a book to anyone. Let it be recorded then that the
one he sent Roddy was one of his especial treasures, and
the act, like mercy, " Blessed him that gave and him
that took."

Mr. Purcell himself had restless nights and pained
days. His meagre strength was failing him, but his face
was happier looking than it had ever been. The liberty
with which Christ sets the captive free was his. He had
fought his way back to the faith of his fore-folk, and
once more the " angel faces smiled which he had loved
and lost awhile ! "

One day he told the Doctor the story of his life. It

was one of bitter disappointment. Friends, hopes, position, and health had been taken from him. " I was flung in the dump heap of life," he said, " a useless log waiting and longing for the end—hoping the end would be oblivion."

" Not oblivion," the Doctor assured him, " but warm fellowship and fullest understanding. It's strange how we poor mortals clamour for a human friend," and then he went on to tell him of a woman whom he had been visiting that day. She was dying, but her concern was not for herself but for those she was leaving. " I've committed my soul to God," she said, " but you ken, Doctor, Jeannie, my oldest lassie, can keep the house and look after the others, but—but Jeannie and her faither—never—get on—together."

" ' Can't you leave Jeannie and her father to God, the God you are trusting your own soul to ? '

" She looked at me and then said slowly : ' That's true, Doctor, but—but *I'd rather leave Jeannie with yourself.*' "

Mr. Purcell laughed softly, but there was a dim look in his eyes.

" I'm afraid there are more of us like that poor woman, Doctor. We'd feel ever so much safer with yourself."

" I must tell you the story of the Minch again," the Doctor replied, and then he sighed, for he was the most human of men. After a little he began :

" 'Tis the weakness in strength, that I cry for ! my flesh, that I seek
In the Godhead ! I seek and I find it. O Saul, it shall be

A Face like my face that receives thee ; a Man like
to me,
Thou shalt love and be loved by, for ever : a Hand
like this hand
Shall throw open the gates of new life to thee ! See
the Christ stand."

When the Doctor prayed he neither changed the
tone of his voice nor his language, but as to a seen
friend so did he speak to the Unseen. And as Mr.
Purcell listened he was strangely moved.

In September the weather was sultry and close.
October, one hoped, would be less exhausting. It was
not.

When on a certain Thursday the Doctor came to
No. 10 he found his friend in bed.

"I think I'm due to cross the Minch," he said with a
little smile. The Doctor gripped his jaw—words are
useless things.

"I've been setting my house in order," Mr. Purcell
went on. "I hope you'll take my books. From careful
inquiries I find that if the little kite-maker could be
taken to London something might be done to help him.
. . . I don't know if the gift of life is always desirable
. . . but we, especially when we're young, believe it is."
Then he entrusted to his friend an account of his
worldly affairs. He had an annuity which died with
him, but there was enough saved to send Roddy to a
specialist and to pay all deathbed expenses.

"I've been very selfish," he said reproachfully,
"wasting money on myself, helping no one, grudging
the loan of a book even to you."

"Tut, tut," the Doctor said with his comforting

chuckle, " you never let me go without lending me a book."

" I hated doing it at first."

" All the more honour to you then." The Doctor refused to be shocked by this confession. Constraint was at an end between these two.

" When the end comes you'll see me off," Mr. Purcell begged.

" I'll see you off," the Doctor promised.

" And—and perhaps—perhaps you'll send up a little prayer that when I cross the Minch my crossing may be favourable."

The Doctor nodded. After a bit he went on : " Our Lord went alone through the darkness of death so that when our turn came He might come with us. Not lonely the way when we have His company."

" I'm resting on that," Mr. Purcell said. He was a great scholar and a great gentleman, and he died with the simple faith of a trustful child. Neither he nor the Doctor ever discussed creeds or doctrines.

It was on the first week of November that the Doctor " saw him off." By Mr. Purcell's own request the Doctor read over him the noble words : " It is sown in dishonour, it is raised in glory ; it is sown in weakness ; it is raised in power. . . . So when this corruptible shall have put on incorruption, and this mortal shall have put on immortality, then shall be brought to pass the saying that is written, Death is swallowed up in victory."

For him the crossing of the Minch had been the entrance into fullest and most wondrous fellowship.

THE DOCTOR'S ALLOTMENT

" LET not your heart be troubled . . . I will not leave you comfortless . . . I will come again."

The Doctor's voice was full of tender compassion as he read words which have been comforting torn hearts ever since the Lord Jesus Christ first uttered them in the upper room in Jerusalem.

And John Anderson needed comfort, for he had, that dreary November day, buried his wife Jean, his comrade and helper for almost fifty years. To the old man left alone the world seemed a bewildering place and lonely beyond all telling.

During the long years of their married life it was Jean who had legislated for the family. John earned the wages (he was a gardener), but Jean spent them thriftily and wisely, making every sixpence do the work of a shilling, always putting aside a little for sickness or old age.

Their two children, a son and a daughter, were both married and had homes of their own now ; the girl had gone with her husband to Vancouver, the son had entered Dewar's Mills as a boy and had risen now to be a foreman.

After their bairns had left them the old couple clung ever closer and closer to each other, sharing each other's very thoughts. The old-age pension and the produce of their garden kept them in comfort. Their lives were peaceable and content. And now Jean was gone !

John could not believe it. When sleep overcame him and he closed his eyes for a few minutes he thought it was all a bad dream. Surely Jean was there in her old chair, sitting on the other side of the hearth, knitting or sewing, for her hands were never idle.

But Jean wasn't there. Her chair was empty. It wasn't a bad dream—it was true ; Jean had gone. When friends urged him to try to sleep and told him sleep would do him good he shook his head. " The sleep may be a' richt but the wakin' is—is—awful. I dinna want to sleep."

The Doctor, who had himself lost his wife and knew the loneliness of life, could enter into the stricken man's sorrow with fullest understanding ; and he could read to him as one having had personal experience of it : " Let not your heart be troubled, neither let it be afraid." Full well did he know that old John's heart was both troubled and afraid.

When the stir and confusion of the last sad days had passed, when neighbours no longer came into the little house, the question arose : " What was to be done with the old man ? "

His son George had married Margaret Duff, daughter of the former foreman, and they lived in a house all too small for them in No. 7 Mill Lane. They had a family of growing youngsters, and though George's wages were good they were all needed, for Margaret was handicapped by bad health.

George immediately offered his father a home with themselves, but Margaret was less cordial. " When a woman-body is left alane she can fill in her time wi' knitting or sewing, but an auld man is a sair difficulty, and grandad is as helpless as a bairn. He can dae naething for hissel. Ay, I suppose we'll hae tae tak' him, though God kens I hae enough tae dae already." And she sighed bitterly.

saying themselves over and over in the Doctor's remembrance as he went home. Life without something to do is a dreary, pointless affair—but what could old John Anderson do ?

The Doctor was still wrestling with the problem when his eye lighted on a bill in the shop window of James MacRae, the ironmonger :

" The market garden belonging to the late James Brodie is to be broken up into allotments, and all who wish to rent a plot are invited to apply within for further particulars."

Twice he read the bill, and then he entered the shop and calmly told the ironmonger that he intended taking an allotment, that it was an answer to his prayer, and would he kindly give him all particulars as per the bill in the window.

The Doctor had a thousand ways of making folk love him, perhaps one of his most endearing was the matter-of-fact way he claimed their help, though he never asked help for himself. So he and James MacRae disappeared into the back shop and the " loon," who was ordered to attend to the counter, afterwards reported that the " boss " and the Doctor had a long long talk in the back shop. At first his boss's voice had been raised as if he were angry, but by-and-by he got more friendly-like, and " at the hinner end the twa were laughing and the boss was collecting a puckle rakes and spades and things, and saying, ' I'll send the loon ower wi' them to the allotment the morn's morn.' "

It was reported by folk who didn't know any better that James MacRae's heart was as hard as the garden implements he sold. But the Doctor knew differently !

March that year came in like a lamb. Sunshine filled

the street when the Doctor marched into No. 7 Mill
Lane, without knocking and demanded that old John
would come out for a walk with him. He assured him
the air would do him good, and Margaret, who had
been trying to bake oatcake bannocks, thankfully
seconded the scheme.

She helped old grandad into his overcoat and looked
rather pitifully after the old man as he crept along by
the Doctor's side. She had not realised how frail and
old he was, nor how slow was his step.

Meantime the Doctor was saying in a mysterious
voice : " I have something I want your counsel about
John."

John looked surprised.

The Doctor lowered his voice. " I have taken an
allotment." He nodded, his eyes dancing with fun.

John's face showed a faint interest. " I didna ken
there were allotments," he said rather wistfully.

" I want you to come and see it now," the Doctor
went on, and gave his companion some particulars.
" I'm thinking of planting strawberries and rasps," he
finished up airily.

" But this is no' the time to plant them," John said
in consternation. " Fruit trees and bushes should be
planted in the back end o' the year. Ye should plant
early tatties, and the important thing in planting tatties
is the richt use o' spade and fork. Is yer grun' trenched
or half-trenched ? Afore ye plant yer tatties ye wad
need to be sure o' that. What kin' is the grun' ? Is't
clay or heavy soil or sandy soil ? Ye can pit on a puckle
bone meal——"

The Doctor held up his hands in horror. " Such
knowledge is too great for me, too high to understand,"

he quoted. "I'm afraid of my allotment now, John! I'll make a present of it to you. Yes, yes, the very thought of it scares me. Man, do you know I'm quite capable of planting bulbs upside down."

By this time they had reached the allotment field and John's eyes brightened with interest as he looked about.

"That's my plot, that one near the wall," the Doctor said.

John examined the soil. "Better o' a guid dressing o' farm manure and syne a top dressing o' chemical."

He took off his overcoat. "Hae ye a spade handy, sir?"

Strange to say the Doctor had; he also had a fork and a hoe. John's coat next came off, he rolled up his sleeves, spat on the loofs (palms) of his hands, and, putting his hat more firmly down on his head, he began to dig.

It was late when he returned to Mill Lane. He was carrying his overcoat over his arm and on his shoulder was a formidable number of garden implements. But best of all was the change in the man himself. He held his head erect and his shoulders square; gone was the listless step—gone the dejected mien.

George and the young folks gathered round him while Margaret got his supper ready, and for the first time since Jean's death he found himself someone of importance. They all wanted to hear about where he had been, and they listened respectfully when he told them of the Doctor's allotment and of how he was going to work it for him. He spoke as one having authority too.

He went early to bed because he explained he must be up early. There were some cuttings and plants and bulbs in the old garden at Quarryside he must get for the Doctor's allotment. He must look out his old boots, too, for there was much digging to be done; he had taken home the tools to keep them dry.

He was up before the kitchen fire was lighted next morning, and he could scarcely wait while Margaret boiled the kettle to make him a cup of tea.

"Grandad," she said, laying her hand on his arm, "I'm awfu' pleased you have got something tae dae."

"So am I, lass," he replied.

"I—I was whiles no' very patient wi' ye," she faltered.

"I—I was whiles no' very considerate," he answered generously, meeting her half-way. "Ye see, I had naething tae dae an' I was lonely an' I was missing Jean. But I'm sure Jean wad be glad if she kent that I've gotten something tae dae, an'—an', Margaret, I'll try nae tae be bothering ye ower muckle."

"Dinna say that," she cried, blinking back the tears which stung her eyes.

"It was jist that we didna understand ane anither."

When John returned that evening his old arm-chair was back in its place by the hearth and on the mantelpiece was a screw of the particularly pungent tobacco the old man liked so much. It was Margaret's way of saying, "Let's begin again." Young George brought him a copy of the *Football Times*.

The most delightful part of the whole business was when John met his fellow plot-holders. They were all in a state of pitiful ignorance—worse even than the Doctor. In the old gardener they found a perfect mine of useful information. They consulted him all the time and he gave of his long experience fully and freely. He lent a hand too, and gave practical demonstrations in grafting, transplanting, and similar mysteries.

Joe Dawson saw no reason why rhubarb leaves should not be tied up in bunches like chrysanthemums. "Sometimes ye can tie up the head of a lettuce to improve its heart," John said, with a smile, " but no' rhubarb."

"Aye plant rose trees in pairs," he advised Jim Davidson. " They will grow better when there's twa o' them—everything should grow in pairs if they're to be happy," and he gave a little sigh.

Joe Davidson got the shock of his life when he discovered that strawberries did not grow " on busses like grossarts," and to one and all of his fellow-workers John had to preach patience. " Nature tak's her time," he assured them, " but she does her work."

" She's no' doing muckle for my rose bush," grumbled Dan Ross. " That tree is there since the month of March an' there's no' sign o' growth." Joe, like the rest of his fellow-gardeners, had a vague idea that if he put plants in the ground and watered them lavishly nature would do the rest. It was a revelation to find that the gardeners must do their bit as regards digging, draining, and preparing the soil.

Old John had to restrain a wild desire on the part of Jim Dawson to pull up shalots and spring onions just to see how they were growing.

The Doctor paid a visit now and then to his allotment, and one day he was given four young lettuces, a few spring onions, and a bunch of rosy-red radishes " to take home."

Knowing the Doctor as we do, it does not seem the least likely that the first fruits of his allotment ever reached the manse. How could they when he had to show—and to share them with—first Margaret Anderson and then with that man of iron, James MacRae, who said he was half minded to get a plot for himself, as everyone seemed to be getting so much fun out of the business. Had the Doctor any use for a few brussels sprouts and some cauliflower plants, because this was the time to plant them? And the " loon," who had gone on many a similar errand, was forthwith despatched to the Doctor's allotment.

One recalls with pleasure that the entire Anderson family, many of his fellow plot-holders, and the Doctor all turned out to see old John getting first prize for his sweet peas at the local flower show.

The prize was an oak biscuit barrel, and as John descended from the platform, amid tremendous applause, he made straight for that part of the hall where his son and his son's wife were sitting and handed the prize to Margaret !

There was one there who saw the gracious act and knew all that was behind it. It moved him to wordless wonder as such fragrant deeds must ever move us. He knew the inner history of the past months and knew the special significance of the old man's act, and if Margaret's eyes were full of tears they were happy tears, and she said and meant it too that she was a proud, proud woman and that never had she got a present she liked so much.

When the Doctor heard this he shook his head sadly, but his eyes twinkled. " *These women !* " he said, and left the matter there. But he did not really feel sad. He was remembering words out of the old Book : " I will not leave you comfortless—let not your heart be troubled, neither let it be afraid."

A DAY WITH THE DOCTOR

THE Doctor selected his heaviest staff out of the hall-stand, and from this Janet, his house-keeper, " jaloused " he was setting off on a long round of visits. She begged him to take his waterproof.

" Why ? " he asked with a laugh. " It's a fine morning—not the least like rain."

She murmured something about it " being mair becoming like " ; the fact was she did not approve of the Doctor's new summer suit. It was a " jacket one " " weel enough for the assistants or for the young minister but no' for the Doctor."

The Doctor was quite aware of this and took a mischievous delight in drawing attention to his garments.

She shook a sorrowful head as she watched him depart. He was taking the road that led to the country where so many of his congregation dwelt. " Dear knows when he'll get his next bite or sup," she murmured to herself— but she was not really anxious. No.

People liked to look at him as he passed ; he was everywhere respectfully and gladly greeted. They knew him to be a man among men and a man of God. Even Dan Cormack, the grocer, who " sat under another minister," and one of a sterner sect, said : " It does me good just to see him passing along the street."

Women young and old looked after him with warmth in their faces and affection in their hearts. They hoped, rather anxiously, that on this day he'd show a little common sense and keep his pockets buttoned and not lend a sympathetic ear and an open hand to every gangrel-body who chose to pitch a plausible and lying tale.

There was no blinking the fact that despite the innumerable number of times he had been " done," he fell an easy prey to the very next beggar.

Maggie Anderson, ostensibly taking in a milk bottle, seized the opportunity to watch him to the end of the street. She sighed impatiently at what she saw.

Mary Stewart, the old tinker wife, who had been in gaol times without number, was coming along. She carried neither her usual basket of tins and dishes nor the bag of rags—for Mary had but that morning come out of gaol and was penniless and friendless too. Her clan had moved out of the town where they had been spending the winter " to gie the bairns some eddication," and she knew that in the miserable room she called " home " there would be neither fire nor food. If only she could raise the price of a dram—she thought desperately—and behold here was the Doctor. She knew him of old for an easy prey !

Maggie Anderson did not hear the conversation which took place. When she joined them, she was just in time to see certain coins of the realm passing from one hand to another.

" Dinna gie her money, Doctor," she pleaded. " She'll only put it to a bad use. She's jist new oot o' the lock-up."

Mary seized the opportunity to slip down a side street calling out as she went, " An' I winna—I'm off to get a puckle coal an' a loaf."

The Doctor looked at Maggie with a reproachful eye. " I know she's just out of gaol," he said. " She was telling me about it—she was telling me too that she is penniless. Maggie, if we were in her place, old and friendless and poor, wouldn't it be a temptation to take a dram and forget everything? And a dram needs no cooking—it's ready! But she has promised she will buy groceries and make herself some food."

"Humph!" Maggie snorted. "I'm sure if I thocht she was really hungry I'd gie her a plate o' broth an' a 'piece'."

"Yes do, Maggie," he said eagerly. "Ask her when you see her coming back," and he left Maggie who had come out to scold remaining to offer hospitality.

*   *   *   *   *   *

Meantime he continued his way, which led him first up the riverside and then through a tract of moorland. He stood for a moment drinking in the beauty of sky and hill and listening to the cry of the muirfowl.

A boy who had been lying on a heathery bank knew by the screaming of the peewits that someone was approaching; it might be someone who did not approve of the company he was keeping. He had just been riding forth with the Knight of Ivanhoe and was an entranced spectator when the Lady Rowenna said in clear and distinct tones these words: "I bestow on thee this chaplet, Sir Knight, as the meed of valour assigned to this day's victor"; here she paused a moment, and then firmly added, "And upon brows more worthy could a wreath of chivalry never be placed"; and behold by some magic the Knight of Ivanhoe was he—Wattie Murray, herd laddie in the farm of Broadlea!

"What are you doing, Wattie?" asked the Doctor, all unconscious of these heroic deeds. Before the boy

could reply a long pain-laden wail rang out followed by
a series of short, yapping barks.

Man and boy listened and their faces grew grave.

" It's a hurt dog," said the Doctor.

" It's Tweed," said Wattie, " an' he's caught in a
trap—an'—an'—I never missed him—I—I was—reading that book."

" The sound is coming from the hillside," the Doctor
said still listening. Wattie, after listening too for an
instant, said : " Ye're richt, sir—I'll awa'."

The Doctor, who had been born and brought up in
the country, followed him. Full well did he know the
difficulty of releasing an animal from one of these cruel
traps. He was glad he had his heavy stick, but just to
" mak' siccar " he armed himself with an old railway
sleeper which had been doing duty as a bridge across
a burn, and followed Wattie's flying figure.

The trap, baited with an ancient rabbit, had been
cunningly concealed among a heap of boulders. Wild
cats were invited to partake ! Poor Tweed, attracted by
the smell, had nosed into the place and before he knew
of the danger his fore-paw was clutched by iron teeth
which refused to let go.

" Take care," the Doctor said, when he reached
Wattie. " The dog may bite."

" Tweed winna bite," Wattie said indignantly.
" Tweed's ma chum."

The Doctor said nothing ; but he knew that a pain-
maddened animal might bite even his chum when cruel
teeth are smashing the bones of his foot.

" Here, take this stick," he said, handing Wattie his
own walking stick. " Now——." But Tweed, fearing
further pain, turned furiously on the walking stick and

bit it. The Doctor brought forward the heavy railway sleeper. " Lean your weight on the end of this—I'll get the other end on the trap and we'll force the teeth open. Steady now—that'll do it ! I'll keep the stick in and the trap open and try to get the dog to take out his foot —it's probably numb."

It only took a few seconds, but they were seconds fraught with anxiety, not the least of which was to get Tweed to do his part.

" Now then—out with your foot—good dog—good dog ! " Wattie cried. His voice seemed to encourage the dog, as with almost human understanding he pulled his hurt paw from between the iron jaws.

He looked at his deliverers with troubled eyes and then set off, limping on his three legs, his hurt foot leaving a trail of blood drops.

" He'll run hame," Wattie said, his face pale beneath its tan, and man and boy felt as if they were lifelong friends, with Tweed as the bond between them.

Wattie told his mother all about it afterwards as they bathed and bandaged Tweed's paw, and she said she was " black affronted " at Wattie's boldness speaking to the Doctor so free-like ; but when Wattie was not present she was heard to boast outrageously about " oor Watt an' the Doctor, an' the awful time the twa o' them hed getting Tweed oot o' the trap, an' of how Wattie was even now thinking out plans at the Doctor's suggestion for inventing a more humane trap."

Neither the Doctor nor Wattie thought it necessary to mention the word " Ivanhoe," nor the bewitching company one met between the covers of the book.

*   *   *   *   *   *

In the farm-house of Ardmore the Doctor received a rapturous welcome from the farmer and his wife. " A glass of milk and a piece of oatcake an' cheese," said the farmer, " an' you'll wait yer denner, sir, if you please— we have sheep's heid broth the day."

The Doctor, as has been already said, was a country born and bred man, and so could speak as one who knows (a little) of the rotation of crops—the feeding and price of " nowts," and all the many difficulties that beset the farmer who deals in sheep.

Old Jeems Menzies, from Drumcraig, who happened to drop in after dinner, said it was not becoming that the Doctor should know so much. " He should speak on the doctrine o' election and predestination," he grumbled. " A minister's opinion of the price of hay should by richts be—' no' worth a preen.' Oor minister, auld Mr. Crombie—an' me met the ither day an' says he to me, ' That'll be barley ye're takin' in ? ' Wad ye believe me, it was a crap o' aits ! But I dinna blame him—his father was so occupied wi' the affairs o' the Kirk that the laddie's eddication was neglected when he was young."

Jeems was " a nattering [1]-bit body," generally agin the Government, whether civil or ecclesiastical. He bitterly opposed the church union of 1904 and was ready on every occasion to justify his conduct.

" Ye'll no' catch me uniting," he would end up with righteous indigation. He hoped that on this day, of which we tell, the Doctor was duly impressed by his firm stand. Just to make sure he said again : " Ye'll no' catch me uniting."

Doctor Lindsay said " No," and then he paused. After

Nattering = nagging.

a bit he went on : " I was lately visiting the lunatic asylum at Deebridge. It's a sad place. I had a long talk with one of the wardens—he's a member of my church—perhaps you know him, his name is Donald MacMillan."

" I ken him," said Ardmore. " He buys wool frae me for blankets—They're maist awfu' hard on blankets in the asylum."

" He was telling me," the Doctor went on, " that it is not so hard to manage these poor afflicted creatures as one would imagine. I said to him, ' Suppose they all unite against you, what would you do ? ' He laughed and answered : ' *But lunatics never unite.*' "

A dead silence fell on the little company as each was busy with his own thoughts. The Doctor, like the skilled story-teller he was, forebore to " point a moral," but old Jeems, who was quick in the uptake, saw the moral with remarkable clarity. He rose to his feet and said he really must be going.

*   *   *   *   *   *

In the cot-house at Whitegates, Margaret Watson lay dying. The things of earth, the cares and anxieties of life, lay heavy on her and she did not want to go. Her man Sandy was an " ill man " to live with, hard-working and decent but " short in the grain," and the oldest lassie, Jeannie, who would take her mother's place, had no patience with her father's girning ways.

" Jeannie an' her father never got on," Margaret confessed, her eyes full of pain. " An' when I'm awa' I'm feared she'll no' bide if he counters [1] her."

Counters = goes against.

" You are committing yourself to the hands of the Heavenly Father. Try to leave Jeannie and your husband there too."

But there was still the terror of death, and what could the Doctor say to help her. He took out of his pocket a book he had brought specially for her. It was *Pilgrim's Progress*, and he had marked it at the place where Mr. Fearing is facing the crossing of the river.

" And here also I took notice of what was very remarkable ; the water of that river was lower at this time than ever I saw it in all my life ; so he went over at last not much above wetshod."

Afterwards they talked, and Andrew Scott, who was passing, keeked in and reported that the Doctor put up a prayer " standing in the middle o' the kitchen floor wi' his staff in his hand an' the sun shining on his white head an' syne he sang :

> " They in the Lord that firmly trust
> Shall be like Zion hill,
> Which at no time can be removed,
> But standeth ever still."

" Margaret was greeting ; but she was smiling too," he added.

*   *   *   *   *   *

Where the moorland road dips down towards the town the Doctor met Jean Raff, the fish-wife, swinging along with a creel on her back. " You're like myself on your country rounds," the Doctor said with a friendly smile. " How are you, Jean ? "

She sighed gustily. " I'll never be nearer death than since I saw you last, Doctor," she replied solemnly.

" Dear me, I'm sorry to hear it."

" I'll never be nearer death," she repeated. She was enjoying herself far too much to hurry with her tale. Still, if she were too slow, the Doctor might move on and that would never do.

" It was ma heid," she began. " Ma troubles aye begin wi' ma heid."

The Doctor was heard to murmur something about " troubles beginning in one's weakest part." She paid no attention.

" Ma heid was that sair I sent ma dochter Jess to the druggist's to get a pooder (powder) for't—an' when she cam' back I wis in ma bed an' ma heid was like to crack, an' I seys, ' Jess, hurry up an' gie me the pooder.' She's awa' noo to the sink for a clean drap o' watter for the pooder an' she steers it—an' she steers it—an' losh be here !—the more she steers it the more it foams. ' Here,' says she, ' drink it while it's fizzing.' But says I, ' I winna, Jess—this is a by-ordinar pooder—it's no fizzing'—it's foaming. Read the directions on the package.' "

She paused dramatically and eyed the Doctor, pleased to note that he was listening with keen interest. " I'll *never* be nearer ma death, Doctor," she said solemnly. " Guess—ye—fit that pooder was."

" Seidlitz ? "

" No. Neither seddlers nor yet Queen Anne, but jist a *shampoo pooder !* "

He congratulated her on her narrow escape from an untimely death. He made almost superhuman efforts to keep solemn, and doubtless the noise Jean heard after they parted was the Doctor's " sair hoast [1] " from which

[1] Hoast = cough.

he sometimes suffered. She noted with concern he had to wipe his eyes too. " Puir man," she murmured, " he should see aboot his hoast."

*   *   *   *   *   *

Little Alice Thomson was hammering out on the piano with painful slowness and grim determination the first half of " Silvery Waves." No human being could say the sounds she produced were the least silvery or wave-like. The piano, for the sake of warmth, had been brought into the living room the previous winter, an arrangement which called for much forbearance from all concerned.

The family had finished tea, and seeing Alice preparing to execute " Silvery Waves " they had all trickled away. Her mother was the last to leave, and she said : " When Billy comes in from the office tell him to take his tea himself. There's plenty of tea in the teapot and the new scones are between two plates to keep them warm. I'm going to the Work Party."

" I'll tell him," Alice said, continuing her fight with distressing crotchets and minims. It sounded as if she were slapping the piano in the face ! She had successfully banged out a chord when she heard a movement behind her.

" That you Billy ? " she asked. " You're to take your tea yourself. There's plenty of tea in the teapot and the new scones are between two plates to keep them warm."

She did not turn her head. She bent all her energies to meet the fury of the next " Silvery Wave." It demanded fierce concentration.

" That's better," said an appreciative voice at her back.

She swung round on the piano stool and met the eyes of—*the Doctor !*

" I'm enjoying my tea very much," he said chattily. " Almost as much as the music. The scones are scrumptious—so was that last chord. Try those last two bars again—you know the ones that say tum-te-tum in the treble and boom-boom-boom in the bass."

He did not see the little girl's consternation ; he was buttering a second scone. " I feel," he said, taking a bite, " as if I were on the beach at Lossiemouth with the waves breaking on the sand."

" But—but—I thought you were Bill," Alice faltered.

" Bill the Lizard ? "

" No. But my brother Bill."

" Have some tea ? " the Doctor suggested, " and I'll pretend I'm the Mad Hatter. You're Alice already. Let's have a tea-party."

Alice is a grown-up young lady now but that tea-party was one she will never forget ; neither will she forget how the Doctor stood by her while she wrestled once more with the chords of " Silvery Waves," and how he helped her and showed her they weren't so very difficult after all. The memory is a precious and a fragrant one.

At Woodend Road the Doctor took a short cut which landed him at the top of High Street, but also landed him almost in front of Miss Eliza Smith, an ancient spinster, with many grievances, one of which was that the Doctor did not visit her more frequently. The Doctor admitted it and then added with a twinkle in his eye : " My visiting is like Mr. Brown's shaving—

regular but not frequent," and Miss Smith was obliged to laugh, for the man in question only shaved every Saturday night. By the time she was done of laughing she discovered that the Doctor was half-way down the street, a characteristic way he had of ending an interview.

*   *   *   *   *   *

Maggie Anderson was ready to tell him : " I got hold o' auld Mary an' she took a good denner an' she's sober ! "

" Thank you," said the Doctor, so gratefully Maggie firmly resolved to go on with the good work.

The death of a summer day always saddened the Doctor. Those gay comrades. the fire and the lamp-light, deserted him in summer and the Manse seemed full of ghosts and very lonely. He shrank from entering it.

Just as he was reaching his own gate a young man who had been approaching from the opposite direction reached the gate too.

" Hugh MacDonald ! "

" Doctor Lindsay ! "

In the miraculous way in which only he could manage it, the Doctor's weight of years fell from his shoulders and his face became young, his voice vigorous, as he shook hands. " You're coming to the Manse ? Come away." This was one of his old assistants now in a charge of his own who, passing through the town, had turned aside for a little to see his beloved old Bishop.

The Doctor's supper, which always consisted of a glass of milk and a boiled egg, was waiting for him. He viewed it with marked dislike. " I won't take it," he said defiantly. " Milk for babes but strong meat for men. Haven't you any cold meat, Janet ? Well, bring it and let's have tea."

" You'll not sleep a wink if you'll have tea," Janet ventured to remind him.

If you think this " halted " the Doctor you're quite wrong. With a merry twinkle in his eye he quoted :

" ' For every one that useth milk is unskilful in the word of righteousness ; for he is a babe.' I'm not a babe ! "

Long and intimate was the talk that followed as the two men sat in the study smoking, and as the Doctor said afterwards, " *One* was striking repeatedly when we parted."

" How did you sleep last night, sir ? " Janet asked.

" I didn't," the Doctor said rather ruefully, and then throwing back his head he added with a laugh : " *But— it—was—worth—it !* "

"BEFORE YE ASK HIM"[1]

I

MONDAY morning in the Manse—a dreary day! This particular morning of which we would tell was one of the four days in the year that the minister, the Rev. John Gordon, particularly dreaded. It was settling up day.

Forty pounds from the central fund for each of the three quarters—thirty-three for one—there was no supplement —the question was would he be able to pay his debts?

Jaded and tired with his previous day's work he might be, still he set this Monday apart for a task which made him sick with apprehension.

He had the bills collected on the desk. He cast a quick glance over them and selected what he knew to be the coal bill. In a manse it is always a problem to know whether the study is to have a fire and the dining-room none ; or if the dining-room is to have one while the study is cold. Every minister's wife had her own way of solving the problem. . . . In John Gordon's study a little fire blazed cheerily. He looked reproachfully at it and then at the coal bill. He then decided a study fire was extravagance for the coal bill was terrifying.

The grocer's bill came next. Things were still dear. Bacon—a luxury got only at communion times or when a foreign missionary came round to plead for funds— was one-and-six. New Zealand butter—that boon to worried housewives—had not come then on the market. Flour, oatmeal, lentils, margarine—homely fare, surely, but all mounting up into a grim total, with the baker's bill in close attendance.

[1] The time of this sketch was 1915.

His eyes were worried as he lifted the next account and glanced first at the total and then at the items. It was the shoemaker's bill. Yes, yes, he knew "better shoon than sheets," better too that young folk should rend their garments rather than their hearts, but—— !

One can do pitifully little about shoes. A deft-handed woman can turn and re-make a garment but shoes defy her. "Four-and-sixpence for soling and heeling," why there wasn't a single week but had its share of these.

The chemist's bill—he had been acutely aware of it all this time and now he lifted it. Bobby, the youngest child, had been ailing all the winter. He had been ordered nourishing food, cream and cod-liver oil. Was this the last bill? No, here was the milk one, and grimly he noted its total. Cream for the little sick child, milk for the growing bairns, one dare not curtail the supply of milk, whatever one might do as regards the butcher's bill. Even so, it too was big.

He totalled up the whole and discovered the forty pounds were all but gone. The new coat he had planned for his wife must wait. A pile of book catalogues he had been hoarding, found themselves suddenly in the waste-paper basket, and then the door opened. His wife, white-faced and anxious, entered.

"Bobby isn't—isn't—so well this morning," she said. "The doctor wants to speak to you. I know quite well he wants to suggest an operation and a nursing home, and oh, John, whatever *shall* we do?"

It speaks volumes for her anxiety that she did not ask about the bills.

II

It was a bitterly cold morning. Outside the Greenhill Nursing Home a haggard-faced woman was walking

up and down, down and up, glancing every minute at
the clock on a neighbouring church steeple, and then
turning her eyes on the windows of the home.

At twelve they had told her she might call and hear
how her little son had stood the operation which was to
be performed at eleven o'clock.

Were ever hours so slow? Were ever moments so
leaden footed? She would walk to the end of the street
she told herself and come back again. Perhaps by that
time the minute-hand of the lazy clock would have
moved a fraction of a second, she was sure the hour one
was static.

Passers-by glanced curiously at her anxious face;
some wondered how she could linger about on such a
cold day; some pitied her; no one spoke to her except
one gentle old man with a saintly face and silvery white
hair who had just come out of the nursing home.

She was so absorbed in her own misery she did not
notice that he had stopped and was looking earnestly
at her.

"Are you in trouble?" he asked gently. "Forgive
an old man's curiosity, but maybe I could help you."

She started and looked inquiringly at the stranger;
one glance assured her that it was no idle curiosity
which had prompted him to speak.

"My little boy——" she began, and then she choked.

"Yes, yes," he nodded understandingly. "In—in—
there?"

She swallowed and presently said: "Yes." Then
she glanced at the clock. "They're operating on him
this morning. . . . Just now, in fact. . . . They said
—I might call at twelve—and—I'd—hear—how—he—
is—and—how—he—stood—the—operation. But it's

only eleven yet. It's been eleven for such a long time."
She turned her haggard eyes to look wistfully at the
church clock.

The Doctor looked at her with tender pity. " Ah—
those mothers ! " he said. " No need to ask them
' Could ye not watch with Me one hour ? ' They could
watch all night and all day too ! Will you allow me
share your watch ? I have been visiting a sick friend
in there and I can assure you that the doctors and
nurses are the best you could possibly have. I know
the head surgeon, too—Sir David Rae."

" That's the man that's—that's—operating on Bobby,"
she told him eagerly.

" Bobby is in good hands, then," the Doctor said
with so much firm assurance Mrs. Gordon, Bobby's
mother, felt her troubled spirit calmed and her heart
strengthened.

In response to his question about the child, she told
the Doctor of his illness. Her husband was a minister
in a remote Highland parish, and when Bobby fell ill
they had thought his trouble would yield to home
remedies. When it did not, they had called in the
doctor, and he had arranged that the child should be
sent to the city to Sir David Rae to get his advice. A
short tale but a poignant one.

He asked a few more questions, and in the answering
of them and in the pacing up and down, time, which
had seemed so slow, did at last move on. With a little
start of surprise she said : " Why, it's twelve o'clock."

" Yes," he nodded, " we can go now and ask for the
bairn."

If she felt surprised at the way in which he identified
himself with her she said no word. She was only

conscious of a sense of peace and reliance from his mere presence. She was soon to find out what going to the home in the Doctor's company meant; the great surgeon, Sir David Rae, came himself to speak to them.

"He's all right," he said, in answer to the Doctor's inquiries. "I didn't know he was one of your cases," he said, with a quizzical look at the Doctor.

"I didn't know myself till eleven o'clock this morning," the Doctor admitted with a smile, and Sir David, who knew the Doctor's ways, smiled too. Then turning to the child's mother, who had been standing timidly by the door, he said in warm friendly tones : "The youngster stood the operation very well. I have left a splendid nurse with him, and you may have a peep at him this evening about seven o'clock. Just a peep, remember, for he may be sick after the chloroform."

Her haggard face grew bright as she listened. "Thank you, sir," she said briefly, and slipped out.

The clock in the church tower recorded that it was twenty-six minutes past twelve, but to Mrs. Gordon it seemed as though a whole eternity had rolled between her coming in and her going out.

III

When Mrs. Gordon returned to the nursing home at seven o'clock she was shown into a waiting room and told that Miss Walters, the head of the home, would see her presently.

She wished her lips would stop trembling—she wished her heart would not leap into her throat at the sound of every passing footstep—she wished nursing homes hadn't that sweet sinister smell of chloroform always lurking about in their passages.

Then the door opened and Miss Walters appeared—
a middle-aged woman with a strong kindly face and a
cheerful smile.

" Mrs. Gordon ? " she inquired. " Sit down for a
minute please. Yes, the little boy stood the operation
all right, he's a plucky little chap. But we think it
would be better that you should not see him to-night.
No, no, there's nothing wrong—everything went as well
as could be expected, but we find he has very little
reserve strength, and that means he'll take longer to
come round." She smiled with the cast-iron cheerful-
ness of the professional nurse. She fixed a shrewd pair
of eyes on the face of the other woman and said : " I
suppose you have been keeping up his strength with
nourishing food all this time ? "

" I—have—tried—my—best," Mrs. Gordon stammered, and the other, looking at her shabby clothes, her
work-worn hands, regretted her question.

" Does it mean Bobby is not rallying ? " Mrs. Gordon
asked.

" No, no, he's rallying all right, and in the morning, if
things go as we expect, you'll certainly get in to see him."

Mrs. Gordon's eyes were smarting with unshed tears.
It was not so much what Miss Walters had said as what
she had *not* said that filled her with apprehension. As
she turned into the cold street her heart was bitter. God
had forgotten to be gracious. She wondered if there
were a God at all. Men, women and helpless little children were at the mercy of blind fate, and what was the
use of struggling on any longer ? One wasn't given a
fair deal, and what was she to say in the telegram to
her husband ?

If there had been room in her heart for any feeling

except misery, she might have wondered how did she happen to meet the Doctor again. But anxiety about Bobby had made her lose her capacity for wonder and then anything can happen.

One glance at her face told him all he needed to know. . . . Though he spoke no word, his silence was wholly sympathetic and presently she began to speak. She spoke bitterly. Thoughts and words she had kept pent up now came forth in a stream, and he did not strive to check her. " Congregations are so cruelly exacting," she said. " Though they knew Bobby was ill, though they knew we were poor," she laughed (he would have preferred that she cried), " they insist on coming to the manse for contributions for every possible and impossible collection. They all advised us to get special advice for Bobby, but not one of them ever suggested a way by which we might pay. And if I weren't present at every meeting of the Women's Guild and the Girls' Club and the Work Party they took me to task as if I had no right to stay at home and nurse my sick bairn, and now . . . Bobby . . . Bobby ! "

Her cry was exceeding bitter ; the old Doctor felt a lump in his throat. Gently he took her by the arm and he was glad that she did not seem to notice he was leading her towards his manse.

She only realised her surroundings when he opened the door and showed her into a study where a bright fire and a comfortable chair gave her welcome all the greater because of the cold and cheerlessness of the outside world.

" You'll keep an old man company for a little," he pleaded. A little table was drawn up close to the fire, and the smell of savoury food made her suddenly conscious of the fact that she had not had a meal since breakfast time, and then it was a mere cup of tea.

"You know Paul was a sensible chap," the Doctor went on, poking the fire into a cheerier blaze. "You remember though he didn't know a single thing about sailing a ship he took command of one during a storm, and the first thing he did was to tell the crew to cheer up and take some food. 'Fourteen days have you tarried and continued fasting,' he told them. Now they must eat and be of good cheer."

His kindness, his understanding made her heart full to bursting. To please him she tried to swallow bite and sup, and after a bit she found it was not so difficult. Dwellers in manses have much in common, and they found many bonds of interest. "Congregations are so unreasonable and so exacting," she repeated.

He shook his head sympathetically. Not once, though she had said many a bitter thing, did he chide her. "You remember old General Booth's advice to his hearers. 'Put yourself in the other fellow's place.' It's simply that they forget to do that. *They don't think.* Oh, I know, and once when I was younger than I am to-day and hasty in my judgments I decided that God had forgotten to be gracious, that no servant of His had ever been so deeply afflicted nor had had such an unkind congregation."

"When I was a young minister in my first charge ministers' salaries used to be paid every six months, and in spite of careful budgeting our expenditure always exceeded our income, and there was no margin for sickness or holidays.

"We had four little folks by this time, and I needn't tell you how careful we had to be. Well, one winter the two eldest fell ill, and the doctor said : ' Scarlet fever.' The two younger children and myself went into lodgings for fear of infection, while my wife and the nurse stayed in the manse."

He paused living again that old unhappy time. Then he shook his head. " Like you, I thought the congregation might wonder how was my salary to stretch out to meet these extra expenses. No one said a word. They all said they were sorry ; they asked us what could they do to help us, and that's always a stupid thing to do. Folk should look and see what you need, and then get busy and *do* it. No one said ' How are you off for money ? ' and bills were pressing.

" I prayed about it, but no answer seemed to come, and the Devil, ever ready when we are depressed, whispered to me that God had forgotten all about us, and do you know I nearly believed him ?

" I remember one evening when the scripture portion for the day was ' Your Father knoweth what things ye have need of before ye ask Him,' I closed the Book— I didn't believe it.

" I lay awake all that night wondering how I was to manage, and then the thought came to me that I would ask a loan from a wealthy old elder of mine. I hated going. Only the memory of our need gave me courage to enter his house. I found him busy at his desk, and just to gain time I began to speak of church matters.

" After a bit I noticed he was looking rather searchingly at me. ' I have been thinking about you quite a lot these last weeks,' he said, and then he turned to the papers on his desk. ' I have been making my will, and in it I am leaving you a little legacy. Now I begin to think would it not be better that you should have it now than wait till I am dead.' . . .

" I could not speak for a moment. Floods of thought overwhelmed me and made me ashamed. A Heavenly Father who did not care—a congregation who did not think—I knew not what to say when I remembered this !

" When I could speak, I made a clean breast of things to him, and I asked the Father to forgive me, and I promised that never, never again would I doubt Him nor think He had forgotten what things I needed."

The Doctor poked the fire—refilled her cup, and did not notice she was fumbling for her hanky. But he saw in her softened eyes that he had not told his story in vain and in the prayer which followed the Heavenly Father, who, whiles, must feel pity for His poor blundering short-sighted bairns, seemed very real and very near. As Mrs. Gordon listened there stole into her heart the firm conviction that all would yet be well—that all *was* well with the child.

*   *   *   *   *   *

Bobby was better in the morning, and his mother saw him for five precious minutes, and the little chap was able to point with wondering eyes to a prancing Arabian steed with flashing glass eyes and dilated nostrils that must have galloped from Fairyland right to the foot of his bed. Sir David asked very humbly might he get a ride on it some day, which made Bobby laugh. " The child has rallied marvellously," Sir David told Mrs. Gordon. But the Doctor was not surprised ; the Father Who knew what we needed even before we asked for it, had sent the child the needed strength.

A fortnight later the Doctor saw off Bobby and his mother. Bobby was hugging the Arabian horse, and the Doctor said " Any man who can carry a horse beneath his one arm can't have much the matter with him." Bobby laughed joyously ; so did his mother. She was going back to her sadly neglected congregation, husband and bairns, but because Bobby was better she heeded not ! Besides, she had told the Doctor that her husband had been appointed Presbytery and Synod Clerk, offices which would add considerably to his salary, " And what a wonderful surprise that was."

" Ministers' wives are wonderful," said the Doctor. " I think there should be a special Heaven for themselves."

" Oh, no," she cried hastily. " Speaking for myself I don't want a special Heaven—I'd rather stay with my man and bairns."

The Doctor's face of affected horror made her realise the meaning of what she had said, and though the laugh was against herself she enjoyed it hugely.

Then she tried to thank the Doctor for all he had done, but words are useless things at best. " He restored my faith in God," she confessed afterwards to one who knew her well. " He made me believe that God knows what things we have need of before we ask Him. Till I knew the Doctor I'm afraid I was not very strong in my belief. But after meeting him and seeing his calm assurance it was easier."

Her husband, to whom she made this confession, took down Milton's *Paradise Lost* and pointed to two lines in it. " There, woman," he said with a laugh, that describes you. The lines were :

> " He for God only,
> She for God in him."

THE DOCTOR GOES FROM HOME

A LETTER from one of the Doctor's old boys lies before me.[1] The writer is now a distinguished preacher, thanks to his old minister. and needless to say the letter he sends is full of love and grateful remembrance of one who did so much for him. He writes :—

" One of the Doctor's winning ways was that when away preaching for any minister, whether in town or country, he always looked up any Elgin people who might be living there, and when he returned home he would go and visit the Elgin friends and tell them all the news."

Then he recalled the story of Jim Mitchell and Walter Anderson, and what these two young fellows owed to this kindly thought and deed. Because of him who tarried with them for a little while one memorable evening the whole current of their lives was changed. This is the story :—

It was Saturday and Jim Mitchell was carefully unpacking his weekly bundle of washing just returned to him from home. Every student knows that though a prosaic bundle of soiled linen may go home, a parcel with hidden romance and adventure, not to mention a letter, lurks within its brown paper bosom when it returns.

" Dr. Lindsay is to be preaching in St. Ninian's Church on Sunday first and be sure you go to hear him. We have given him your address and he said if he had time he'd go and see you. You'll find a few shillings (for stamps) in the toe of your brown socks and I hope you'll like the gingerbread. Mind you sit at your

[1] Gillian Munro.

books in your old jacket. If you must fix on buttons
on your pants please don't do it with old boot laces
which leave a black mark."

"It wasn't a boot lace—it was a bit of parcel twine,"
Jim Mitchell mused, reading his mother's letter.

Jim's co-digger used to regard these washing bundles
with rather wistful interest, though wild horses would not
make him admit it. His mother was dead and there was no
one in his home to secrete shillings in his socks or gingerbread in his pyjamas. His washing went to the laundry
and returned to him with a bill and without a button.

Both lads were students in the Divinity Hall of Glasgow
and both took themselves with the utmost gravity.
They doubted the theology of St. Paul and picked holes
in his grammar. They shook wise young heads over
the Johannine epistles and said really terrible things
about Isaiah. They were very young !

Jim, having been brought up under the Doctor, was
wont to quote his home minister to his friend rather too
often. "I'm tired of hearing about Dr. Lindsay,"
Watt used to say crossly ; he said it so often that at last
Jim ceased referring to his minister, and for that very
reason he did not tell him that the Doctor was to preach
in St. Ninian's Church on Sunday.

But with the wisdom of the serpent if not the harmless-
ness of the dove he laid his plans to go to St. Ninian and
to take his friend with him.

On Sunday morning he said, oh, very casually, " I
hear they're having specially good music at St. Ninian's
to-night. It is said to be the best sung church in Glasgow."

Watt looked at him in blank amazement, for Watt
was an authority on music and was a member of St.
Bennett's choir and sung an excellent and tuneful tenor.

" You are giving me news," he snorted.

Jim went on blandly : " Well—I'm going to hear, anyway."

" And since when were *you* a judge of music—you that don't know ' B ' from a bull's foot ? "

But Jim refused to lose his temper and repeated stubbornly : " I'm going to hear."

Watt lifted the Hebrew grammar he was studying and appeared to be lost in its pages, only Jim noticed he was holding it upside-down.

Presently he threw it down. " Well I don't believe it," he said fiercely. " And though you were to tell me a hundred times over, I wouldn't believe it. St. Bennett's is the best, and just to prove it I'll come with you to St. Ninian's."

Jim bent and poked the fire—which was quite unnecessary—however his face was grave again when he looked up to ask : " Will you really ? "

" I'll come and hear for myself," Watt repeated grimly.

    *   *   *   *   *   *

The church was packed when they reached it and the only available seats were close to the pulpit. The minister was already in his place and the bout of coughing which always seizes a congregation when the first singing is about to be given out was in full swing.

When silence fell the minister rose, the light shining on his silvery-white hair and saintly face.

He gave a quick glance around the crowded pews. A young fellow sitting near the pulpit was convinced that the Doctor's eyes met his and sent him friendly greeting. Because of this his heart swelled high with pleasure so that he found it difficult to join in the first singing. It was the twenty-third psalm, and it was sung to the tune of Evan—the psalm and tune of all Scottish childhood. By the magic of these the folk were bairns again and memories glad and sad came crowding around them.

> " And in God's house forever more
>   My dwelling place shall be."

As the last words died away the Doctor began to pray. The singing had touched his heart ; he was keenly sensitive to music and the folk had sung with heart and voice. In the prayer which followed his hearers still carried with them the warm feeling of being children again, gathering into the Father's house. The Doctor's voice and his language were those of everyday speech—but as he prayed, the depth and tenderness of his nature were revealed and the hearts of his listeners were thus prepared for his message which he brought them.

His text was : " One of the two which heard John speak, and followed him, was Andrew, Simon Peter's brother. He first findeth his own brother Simon, and saith unto him, ' We have found the Messias,' which is, being interpreted, the Christ. And he brought him to Jesus. And when Jesus beheld him, He said, ' Thou art Simon, the son of Jona : thou shalt be called Cephas,' which is, by interpretation, a stone."

In the twinkling of an eye that vast congregation was standing on the banks of the Jordan—hearing John the the Baptist as he looked on Jesus and said : " Behold the Lamb of God." They were with the two disciples who heard him speak and they followed Jesus. One of the two was Andrew and he brought his brother Simon to Jesus. It was the beginning of the Christian Church —two men, each of whom found his brother. The work was begun by Andrew but completed by Christ—that was the theme of the Doctor's discourse, and from it he wove a message which was for the cheer and encouragement of his hearers. Spell-bound the people listened, and they sung the closing psalm to the Doctor's favourite tune of Effingham.

> " His name forever shall endure ;
>   Last like the sun it shall :
>   Men shall be bless'd in him, and bless'd
>   All nations shall him call."

The feeling in the church as the last notes died away was one of deep emotion. The Doctor rose and with the light shining on his head and his hands upraised in blessing, he said :—

> " Oh may we stand before the Lamb,
>   When earth and seas are fled,
>   And hear the Judge pronounce our name,
>   With blessings on our head ! "

It was a favourite benediction but one he only used when he was much moved. That the pew made the pulpit was one of the Doctor's firm beliefs. . . . With the gracious words ringing in their ears the folk went home feeling that though Monday morning and all its worries were already casting a shadow over their spirits they would go in the strength of the message which they had heard that night and their hearts would be strong for the battle of life.

Jim Mitchell and Watt Anderson walked home in silence. At last Watt broke it by saying with all the warmth of his young heart : " That was a great sermon ! "

" Not bad," Jim conceded.

"The singing was good, too," Watt went on, determined to be generous. "It's not so good as St. Bennett's though."

"Well, at least all the congregation sang. They didn't stand listening to the choir," Jim retorted.

This was an old bone of contention, but just at that moment Watt ignored it.

"He can preach—that old minister," he said. "One felt he was so sincere. . . . Quite a simple text, too " (which it was not).

Again they walked on in silence, each busy with his own thoughts. Then Watt said : "Yes, I like that old man. He's thoroughly sound. If your Dr. Lindsay could preach like that old minister I could forgive you for always speaking about him."

In the light of a street lamp Watt noticed that Jim's face looked excited and his eyes were burning to say something which his lips refused to utter.

"I'm glad you liked the singing, Watt," he said at last. "And I hope the next time I ask you to come to St. Ninian's you'll come with a little better grace."

Watt laughed. "Provided of course that the singing is as good as it was to-night and that that old minister is preaching. Do you know his name ? "

They had reached their lodgings by this time. Jim was fitting the latchkey into the lock, and when the door was opened and the light turned on he said, looking at his co-digger with eyes bright with excitement : *" That was Dr. Lindsay, Watt ! "*

*   *   *   *   *   *

The two young men were at tea (with gingerbread) the following evening when their landlady ushered in a visitor. . . . It was the Doctor.

" I promised your mother that if I could manage it I'd look you up, Jim," he said, shaking hands, and radiating all around him that wonderful feeling of friendliness. Years might have robbed him of bodily strength but they could never rob him of his eternal and joyous youth. And youth must ever call to youth !

If you think Jim Mitchell was the proudest young fellow in the whole world you may. He introduced him to Watt Anderson, and because the Doctor " had a way with him " in five minutes Watt was his slave for life.

" Yes, of course I'll have a cup of tea, and was that really Elgin gingerbread, and how did Jim know it was his favourite cake ? And as they took their tea he told Jim little bits of home news and news by " word o' moo " is much more satisfying than by the written word. He recalled, too, with a chuckle of delight how in the Bible class in Jim's day he had set the class hunting for " the wiles of the devil." He himself could only manage a dozen. " Do you remember, Jim, how you appeared the following Sunday with a list of twenty ? "

Jim laughed. " And do you remember what you said, sir ? ' It is evident that my young friend is better acquainted with the wiles of the devil than I am.' And how the class laughed ! "

And then the Doctor had to hear of their studies, and when his eye fell on the Hebrew grammar with which Watt had been wrestling he adjusted his spectacles and read the passage in English, fluent and scholarly.

Jim glanced proudly at Watt. What had he told him?

*　　*　　*　　*　　*　　*

The Doctor had a word of prayer with the two lads ere he went. They were loath to let him go, but he had

E 2

promised to look up some other friends, he could not wait longer.

Jim, seeing the Doctor had come specially to see him, disappeared into the bedroom to change his jacket and give the Doctor a Scots convoy, and Watt took the opportunity to say—oh, very falteringly, but very earnestly—how much the sermon on the previous night had been to him. " And I didn't want to go," he confessed. " Jim made me by telling me the singing was better than in St. Bennett's."

The Doctor laughed. " But he brought you to church, Watt," he said, " and in the days of old Andrew brought Simon to Jesus. Remember what that meant and it was all part of God's great plan—the forwarding of the Kingdom."

Both lads accompanied him home. Watt, on his own invitation, but to the great content of the others. Neither of the lads could bear to part with the Doctor till at last he said with a laugh : " Be off home now and I'll write you." And he did.

He did more. He went to see Jim's father and mother and he told them all about his visit. Jim's mother complained that her son was no letter writer. " When I ask him has he plenty blankets on his bed, and does he air his flannels, and is his landlady giving him good dinners he pays no attention to me."

The Doctor chuckled. " But he does pay attention to you. . . . He sits at his books in his old jacket ! I saw him do it."

" He's nae a bad loon," Mrs. Mitchell conceded, and blew her nose emphatically. " Aye, aye, Dr. Lindsay, we're glad to hear what you're telling us."

*   *   *   *   *   *

Jim Mitchell and Walter Anderson are lads no longer, but they carry with them the gladsome memory of that wonderful time when they met the Doctor, and with both of them a favourite text is : " He brought him to Jesus." They find it is not quite so simple, after all.

THERE is no time in the whole week so delightful to a minister as Sunday evening; there is no meal so enjoyable as the Sunday evening's supper, not that it's ever anything great or grand, but it can be eaten in leisure, and there is time for talk.

The work of the day is done; bedtime is still some hours distant, and if there is a congenial friend to share the study hearth, to smoke, or talk, or keep silent, just as the mood takes one, then the minister gives a sigh of happy anticipation.

By and by—preferably when he goes to bed—memory will waken, and he will recall with pain things which he might have said and did not; he will remember with equal pain things which he would like to unsay or put in a different fashion—and he cannot now! But these memories are sleeping at the moment; there is only the sense of thankfulness for the hours of rest that lie ahead—the physical delight in the warmth of the fire—the comfort of old slippers—a pipe and a chair that is really an easy chair. And if the occupant of the other fireside chair is like-minded, then indeed the minister is happy.

The Doctor was in this happy case on the Sunday evening of which we would like to tell. His old friend, the Rev. Ian Grahame, was with him.

They exchanged funny stories and discussed texts. It is quite impossible for two ministers to foregather without these things happening!

The Doctor was, of course, convinced that no congregation in all the land was equal to his, and if there was power in the pulpit, then it was because of the help got from the pew.

" They'd make a stone wall preach," he declared, and then they discussed texts and the strange places in which one finds a text sometimes.

The Doctor said : " There is a tree in our town-hall square, my study window looks right out upon it, and it has been preaching to me a sermon lately. Two winters ago a storm broke off a large branch at the point of juncture with the main tree. The branch still hung by a tag, but throughout one whole summer no bud or leaf appeared on it. I thought it was dead ; had I used it as an illustration a year ago, it would have been as an emblem of a man with the tag of outward membership in the Church, but no living hold on Christ. But, to my astonishment, after eighteen months of hanging limp and seemingly lifeless, there, one morning in May, I saw three buds on it and leaves being put forth. If that branch could speak it would say, ' O my soul, thou hast trodden down strength ! ' the strength of the tempest, and the rupture it caused, and wreck it made. It almost made me weep for penitence and joy, because I read this in it : ' Your life may have got low through unwatchfulness, but if ever you're a living branch of the vine there is recovery for you.' " [1]

" It was a text I had used thirty years ago, but I had not seen then the miracle of the torn branches. I was far too doctrinal. I suppose it is the fault of youth. It's as we grow older, we grow simpler."

" You remember," said Mr. Grahame, " the old Highland woman who had listened to a long doctrinal discourse with great joy. Someone asked her : ' Did

[1] From *The Weakness of God*, by Rev. Robert Cowan.

you understand the minister, Margaret?' and she replied, in all good faith, 'The Lord forbid that I would understand the decent gentleman.'"

They were both laughing over this when the door opened and Janet appeared. "It's—it's—old Peter, the pensioner," she said with an apologetic air. "They've just sent a message to say they think he is sinking, but—but—you will not go out more the night, sir? It's cold and it's dark."

The Doctor merely said: "Bring me my boots, please."

"Couldn't you wait till the morning?" suggested his guest.

The old man shook his head, seeing which, Mr. Grahame said: "Well, I'll come with you."

*   *   *   *   *   *

The rose tree which grew beside Peter's door and used to be the pride of his heart, was looking like a neglected child. The nails fastening it to the wall had been wrenched loose by the wind, and the branches waved forlornly; sometimes they tapped on the window as if to summon their old friend to come to their help.

Mactavish,[1] Peter's terrier, came to meet the Doctor as he entered the house (of course without knocking). The dog wore an air of deep perplexity. He could not understand why his master lay in bed all day. He was so worried over this problem that even when his arch enemy, Miss Jane Brodie's cat, gazed over his head with her usual insolent expression as she sat on the top of the water tank, he would only say "Woof" and pass on.

See *The Doctor Visits*, Part III.

Miss Jane was now a fast friend of Mactavish ; she no longer threw brooms at him, which was a good thing. Still, why didn't his master rise and potter about the garden and attend his rose-tree as he used to do? Mactavish had brought in and laid at his bedside an ancient ball, a far-from-reticent bone, and a fur-lined glove which he imagined not without reason was a rabbit. . . . But nothing happened. . . . There are times when a dog must find the ways of human beings very perplexing.

Hopefully he trotted after the Doctor and accompanied him into the bedroom.

*   *   *   *   *   *

Peter's mind was wandering over uncharted seas— over unexplored continents. His old sister who had come to nurse him whispered to the Doctor that he was very low ; his mind was wandering.

Then she bent over the sick man and said in his ear : " It's the Doctor, Peter—Dr. Lindsay. He is come to see you. Do you know him ? "

Peter opened his eyes and they no longer looked dazed. " The Doctor," he said, speaking with difficulty. " I mind how he lauched—the day Mactavish—chased— Miss—Brodie's—cat, an' I said—fit wist—I said ? " he inquired, his voice trailing off weakly. " I—canna— mind—but the Doctor was awfu' cheery."

" He's wandering," his sister said again in scandalised tones.

" No, he's not," the Doctor replied, and then turning to Peter he said : " You remember the day Mactavish chased Miss Brodie's cat and I said Miss Brodie was a daughter of the King—all glorious within ? "

"Aye, aye," Peter said slowly, a pleased smile on his face.

"Then you said: '*Them that auchts her sud flipe her.*'"

Peter gave a queer trembling laugh and suddenly asked: "Where's ma dowg—where's Mactavish?"

The dog, wildly excited at hearing the loved voice asking for him, jumped on the bed and bestowed eager licks of delight on the face and hands of the old man. Peter tried to pet him and to speak to him in his old voice. Dog and man rejoiced over each other and the Doctor was greatly moved.

He had forgotten now how tired he was, and when Mactavish was at last persuaded to lie down at the foot of the bed, the Doctor opened his little Bible and read the gracious words of the fourteenth chapter of St. John. "In my Father's House are many mansions," he read. And so through the lovely words which have comforted the dying throughout the ages.

Peter listened attentively, then he whispered: "I'm —flitting." "I'm—leaving—this auld hoose," and he let his hand fall weakly over his chest.

"You're going to one that is far far better," the Doctor assured him.

Peter smiled, but next moment conscious of the dog at his feet, he said: "I—doot—I—canna—tak'—Mactavish."

"I'll take Mactavish," the Doctor promised him. "He'll miss you, but I'll try to make him happy."

Peter sighed as if well content and fell asleep. The Doctor slipped out; Mr. Grahame had waited for him in the kitchen and together they went back to the manse.

The Doctor leaned wearily on his friend's arm as he

walked along, and again Mr. Grahame said : " You should have put it off till the morning."

" I dared not," he answered. " Once when I was taking a month's preaching for Hugh MacKenzie—you remember Hugh ? "

Mr. Grahame nodded. " Hadn't he a charge in Ross-shire ? "

" Yes. Well one Sunday evening after church I was going back to Hugh's manse when a little tinker lassie came and asked me to come with her to her grand-father's tent. He was very ill and wanted to see a minister. One of Hugh's elders was with me, and he persuaded me—I was willing to be persuaded, I'm afraid—that it would do if I went in the morning. . . . I went in the morning. . . . And the old tinker was dead. . . . I was too late." His voice shook with emotion as he recalled this experience.

" I have asked God to forgive me, and I hope that He has, but I'll never, never, forgive myself. All that I can do now is to go to a sick bed when I'm asked. I dare not wait till a more convenient season."

*   *   *   *   *   *

The study fire was smouldering dully when they returned. The Doctor eyed it with strong disapproval. " Just wait a moment," he said, and disappeared.

Presently there was the sound as of someone briskly breaking sticks, and in came the Doctor with his arms piled high with firewood, the breaking of which as one of his fellow-presbyters has said : " was one of his favourite ploys."

" We'll soon have a cheery fire," he said. " Oh, we're not going to bed," with a glance at the clock. " We haven't begun to talk yet."

" Now," he said, giving a sigh of pleasure, " there's a fire to warm you from stem to stern."

His visit to Peter had sent his own spirit into the unseen. He loved to dwell on Heaven and the life there. " I often wonder who will greet us first on the other side. Do you know I have an idea that Peter's mother will come to meet him. Peter was in many ways a boy always, and I think—I think—that God always sends mothers to greet and welcome their boys when they cross the river."

Silence fell on them, and then very gently Mr. Grahame recalled to him his own wonderful dream [1] : We give it in the Doctor's own words. " I had such a strange dream last night—I think I must tell it to you. I dreamt I was in Heaven, and the queer thing was that I didn't feel a bit happier than I had done many a time on earth. There was not a kent face to be seen, and I felt lonely—dreadfully lonely. But just then I noticed a young man by my side, a tall dignified-looking man with a friendly open face. ' You have just come ? ' He said. ' Yes, sir,' I answered. ' And are you feeling a little lonely ? ' ' Well—yes—I was a little lonely ; but since you have spoken to me, that feeling has gone.' ' Would you like Me to stay with you ? ' He asked. His eyes were wonderful, as if at some time in His life He had known some great tragedy, and on His brow was the mark of an old wound.

" ' Sir,' I said, ' it is what I would like above everything else, I feel—I feel as if I had known You all my life.'

" He stretched out His hand to greet me. There was the mark of an old wound in its palm ; when I looked

[1] The Doctor supplies.

into His face He was smiling ; and then—then—I knew it—was—the—Lord Himself ! "

*   *   *   *   *   *

" I think," Mr. Grahame said, very gently, " I think the first to greet you, Dr. Lindsay, will be your old friend Whom you knew and loved on earth—the Lord Himself."

The Doctor looked at him with a smile.

Printed by The Whitefriars Press Ltd.
London and Tonbridge